AGS

Geometry
Student Workbook

AGS®

American Guidance Service, Inc.
Circle Pines, Minnesota 55014-1796
800-328-2560

©2001 AGS® American Guidance Service, Inc., Circle Pines, MN 55014-1796.
All rights reserved, including translation. No part of this publication may be
reproduced or transmitted in any form or by any means without written
permission from the publisher.

Printed in the United States of America

ISBN 0-7854-2224-2

Product Number 91203

A 0 9 8 7 6 5

Table of Contents

Points and Lines in the Plane

EXAMPLE   Collinear points are located on the same line. Points *C*, *D*, and *E* are collinear.

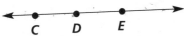

        C   D   E

Study the point, line, line segment, and ray.

A   n   N   T   A   B

Directions   Answer the following questions.

1. How many points are necessary to define a line?   2

2. Given three noncollinear points in space, how many lines can be drawn?   3

3. Given three collinear points in space, how many lines can be drawn?   1

4. Given three collinear points and one other point that is not on the same line, how many lines can be drawn?   4

5. How many endpoints are needed to draw four line segments?   5

6. How many endpoints are needed to draw three line segments?   4

7. How many endpoints are needed to draw six line segments?   7

8. How many endpoints are needed to draw ten line segments?   11

Directions   Tell whether each figure is a point, a line, a line segment, or a ray.

9. Ray

10. Ray

11. line   line segment
   F   G

12. line
  L

13. line segement
  t   D   E line

14. Point
  X

15. line
  F   G
  line segme

Name Date Period

Chapter 1 Workbook Activity 2

Measuring Line Segments

EXAMPLE Measure a line segment by placing the zero mark of a ruler on one end and reading the distance to the other end.

____

The line is 4 inches long.

Directions Measure the following line segments in inches.

1. ____

2. _____________________________

3. ____

4. ___________________

5. __________

Directions Measure the following line segments in centimeters.

6. ____

7. ____

8. ______________________

9. _____________________________________

10. ____

Ruler Postulates

EXAMPLE   Given line *AB*, the number line can be chosen so that *A* is at zero
and *B* is a positive number.

Given two points, *A* and *B* on a line, the number line can be chosen so that
A is at zero and *B* is a positive number.
The distance between *A* and *B* = |3 − 0| or | − 3| $\overline{AB}$ = 3

Directions   Use the Ruler Placement Postulate to calculate the distance between *A* and *B*.

1.

2.

3.

4.

EXAMPLE   If *B* is between *A* and *C*, then $\overline{AB} + \overline{BC} = \overline{AC}$.

$\overline{AB}$ = 3, $\overline{BC}$ = 2, $\overline{AC}$ = 5
$\overline{AB} + \overline{BC}$ = 3 + 2 = 5

Directions   Use the Segment Addition Postulate to prove that *B* is between *A* and *C*.

5.

Copying and Bisecting Angles

EXAMPLE　Angles can be copied exactly using a compass and straightedge.

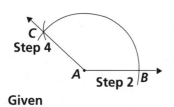

Given

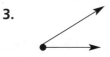

Copy

Directions　Copy each angle using a compass and straightedge.

1.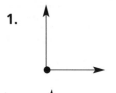

2.

3.

4.

5.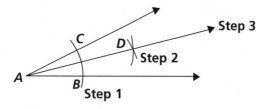

EXAMPLE　Angles can be bisected exactly using a compass.

Directions　Copy each angle. Then bisect the angle you've drawn using a compass.

6.

7.

8.

9.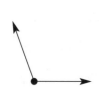

10.

Angle Measurement

EXAMPLE   Angles can be measured exactly using a protractor.

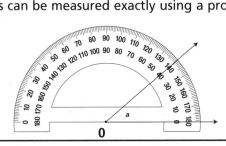

Directions   Measure the following angles.

1.

2.

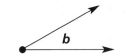

3.

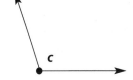

4.

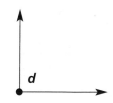

5.

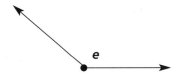

6.

Directions   Classify the following angles as either *acute, right, obtuse,* or *straight.*

7.

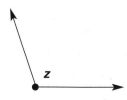

8.

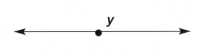

9.

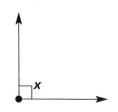

10.

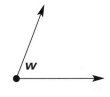

Complementary and Supplementary Angles

EXAMPLE Two angles whose measures add to 90° are called
complementary angles.

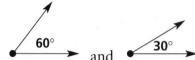
60°   and   30°

Directions Measure the angle shown and then draw an angle that is complementary to it.

1.

2.

3.

4.

5.

EXAMPLE Two angles whose measures add to 180° are called
supplementary angles.

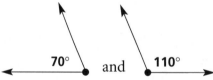
70°   and   110°

Directions Measure the angle shown and then draw an angle that is supplementary to it.

6.

7.

8.

9.

10.

Name _____ Date _____ Period _____

Chapter 1

Workbook Activity

7

Algebra and Angles

EXAMPLE Solve for the missing angles.

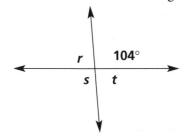

$a + 75° = 180°$ $b + 105° = 180°$ $c + 75° = 180°$
$a = 180° - 75°$ $b = 180° - 105°$ $c = 180° - 75°$
$a = 105°$ $b = 75°$ $c = 105°$

Directions Solve for the missing angles.

1.

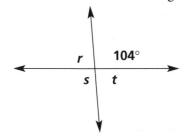

2.

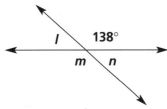

3.

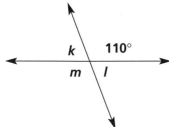

4.

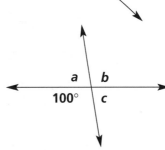

5.

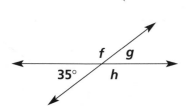

Directions Find the measure of each numbered angle, given m∠2 = 46°.

6. m∠2 _____

7. m∠3 _____

8. m∠4 _____

9. m∠5 _____

10. m∠6 _____

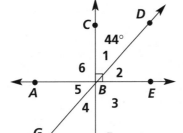

Geometry

Drawing Networks

| EXAMPLE | If you can trace a route in a continuous line without drawing over a section twice, then the route is called a traversable network. |

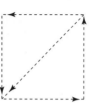

Directions Trace the following networks. Decide whether they are traversable or not and explain how you made your decision.

1.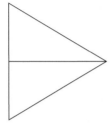

_____

_____

_____

2.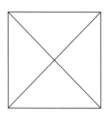

_____

_____

_____

3.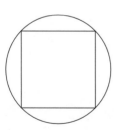

_____

_____

_____

4.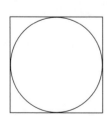

_____

_____

_____

Directions Answer the following question.

5. Who or what might benefit from the use of traversable networks? List as many situations as you can.

Conditionals

EXAMPLE

75°   105°

If <u>two angles are supplementary</u>, then (the sum of their measures equals 180°.)

The underlined part of the conditional, or the "If" part, is the hypothesis.
The circled part of the conditional, or the "Then" part, is the conclusion.

Directions   Write *True* or *False* for each of the following conditionals.
Underline the hypothesis and circle the conclusion.

1. If an angle is less than 90°, then the angle is an acute angle.   _____

2. If two circles have the same radius, then they are equal to one another.   _____

3. If a figure has five sides, then it must contain at least one right angle.   _____

4. If a closed figure has four angles, then the sum of their measures
   must equal 360°.   _____

5. If the measure of one angle created by the intersection of two lines is 90°,
   then all four of the angles created by the intersection of the two lines will
   measure 90°.   _____

6. If your computer doesn't work when you turn it on, then there must
   be something wrong with the processor.   _____

7. If it is snowing outside, then the temperature must be less than
   32° Fahrenheit.   _____

8. If it is raining outside, then you will get wet.   _____

Directions   Use a conditional to explain each situation.

9.

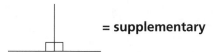

= supplementary

10.

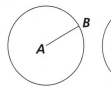

$\overline{AB} = \overline{CD}$

The two circles are equal.

Converses

EXAMPLE

Given Conditional
If an angle measures > 90°,
then the angle is obtuse.

Converse
If an angle is obtuse,
then it measures > 90°.

Directions Write *True* or *False* for each conditional. Then write the converse of each conditional.

1. If an angle is less·than 90°, then it is a right angle. _____

2. If a circle has the same diameter as the length of the side of a square, then the circle and the square are equal. _____

3. If the measures of two pairs of supplementary angles are added together, then the sum will equal 360°. _____

4. If two circles have the same center but different-sized radii, then they are equal. _____

5. If the measures of all four angles of a closed four-sided figure are 90°, then the figure is a rectangle. _____

6. If the measures of two pairs of complementary angles are added together, then the sum is equal to the measures of two right angles. _____

Directions Write *True* or *False* for each converse in problems 1–6.

Directions Write a conditional for each situation.

7. A conditional that is true whose converse is true

8. A conditional that is false but whose converse is true

9. A conditional that is true but whose converse is false

10. A conditional that is false whose converse is false

Lines and Euclid's Postulates

EXAMPLE

Euclid's Postulate 1   A straight line can be drawn from any point to any point.

Euclid's Postulate 2   A finite straight line can be extended
continuously in a straight line.

Euclid's Postulate 5   If one straight line, *t*, crosses two other straight lines, ℓ and
m, four angles are formed. If the two inside angles, *a* and
b, together measure less than two right angles, then the
two lines ℓ and *m* will, if extended indefinitely, meet on the
same side as the two angles *a* and *b*.

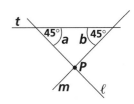

Directions   Use the above postulates to make the following constructions.
List the postulates you use.

1. Draw a square by connecting points *A*, *B*, *C*,
and *D*.

A.   .B

D.   .C

2. Draw a straight line that is parallel to
line *m* and passes through point *X*.
Then draw arrows showing that line
m is extended continuously.

3. Extend lines *a* and *b* to form an
equilateral triangle.

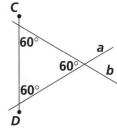

Directions   Use Euclid's Postulates to tell whether the following statements are true. List which
postulates were used.

4. Points *A*, *B*, and *C*
can be joined by
line segments to
form a triangle.

A.

•B

c.

5. There is more than one
line that can be parallel
to line *m* and pass
through point *X*.

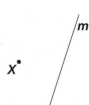

Circles and Right Angles

Euclid's Postulate 3   A circle may be described with any center and distance.

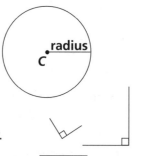

Euclid's Postulate 4   All right angles are equal to one another.

Directions   Use the above postulates to make the following constructions. List the postulates you use.

1. Draw four circles that are equal in such a way that lines connecting the centers of the circles form a square with right angles.

2. Draw a square. Connect the corners to create four right angles.

Directions   Examine the following objects. List the different figures, such as circles, squares, and right angles, that are contained within each object's shape. Write the postulates that you think relate to each shape's construction.

3.

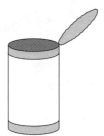

4.

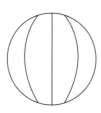

5.

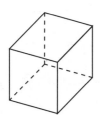

Using Euclid's Postulates

EXAMPLE

Given: a point, *X*, and a segment, *CD*
Draw a circle with *X* as the center and $\overline{CD}$ as the radius.

Euclid's Postulate 3 makes this construction possible.

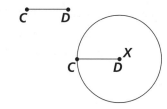

Directions Name the postulate(s) that make(s) each construction possible.

1. Draw a circle with center *A* and radius *AB*. Then draw a circle with center *A* and a radius that is twice as long as $\overline{AB}$.

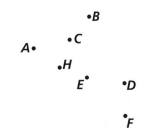

2. Draw line segments connecting points *A* through *H* so that no line segment crosses another line segment.

3. Extend the lines of angle *A* so that four equal right angles are created.

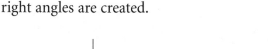

4. Draw three line segments parallel to line segment *AB* through points *X*, *Y*, and *Z*. Each line segment should be 1 centimeter shorter than $\overline{AB}$.

5. Draw a circle with center *X* and radius *AB*. Then draw a triangle and a square, each with sides of equal length and whose corners are a distance $\overline{AB}$ from *X*.

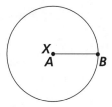

Making Constructions

| EXAMPLE | Draw a triangle with a right angle and two angles that are equal and complementary. |

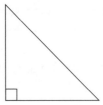

Directions Do these constructions on a separate sheet of paper.
Tell which postulate(s) you used to make each construction.

1. Connect all of the points *A* through *H* with all other points.

2. Given line *m* and point *S*, draw a line that is perpendicular to line *m* and passes through point *S*. Use this line as the radius of a circle with center *S*.

3. Connect points *A*, *B*, and *C* to form a triangle. Then use the length of the shortest side as the radius to make three circles with points *A*, *B*, and *C* as the centers.

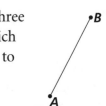

4. Given the line *AB*, draw three different situations in which you could extend the line to include points *C* and *D*.

5. Draw two circles, one with center *M*, one with center *N*, and each with a radius *MN*.

6. Draw four right angles equal to one another.

Directions Connect the points in each way indicated.

7. Connect the points to create four squares.

8. Connect the points to create four triangles.

9. Connect the points to create two rectangles.

10. Connect all of the points with all of the other points.

Axioms and Equals

EXAMPLE	Axiom 1	Things that are equal to the same thing are equal to each other.
		If $a = b$ and $b = c$, then $a = c$.
	Axiom 2	If equals are added to equals, the sums are equal.
		If $a = b$ and $c = d$, then $a + c = b + d$.
	Axiom 3	If equals are subtracted from equals, the differences are equal.
		If $a = b$ and $c = d$, then $a - c = b - d$.

Directions   Name the axiom that gives the reason for each step.

1. $x - 3 = 4$
   $+3 = +3$
   $x = 7$

2. $z + 3 = 4$
   $-3 = -3$
   $z = 1$

3. $y + 10 = 15$
   $-10 = -10$
   $y = 5$

4. $a - 75 = 76$
   $+75 = +75$
   $a = 151$

5. $b + c = d$
   $-c = -c$
   $b = d - c$

6. $b + c = d + c$
   $-c = -c$
   $b = d$

Directions   Solve each problem to find the value of x.
List the axiom you used to solve the problem.

7. $m\angle x + m\angle y = 90°$

8. $m\angle x - m\angle y = 90°$

9. If $m\angle a = m\angle c$ and $m\angle b = m\angle d$, and $m\angle a + m\angle b = 180°$, and $m\angle c + m\angle d = x$, then what does x equal?

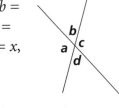

10. If $m\angle x = m\angle y + m\angle z$, and $\angle y$ is complementary with $\angle a$, and $\angle z$ is complementary with $\angle a$, and $\angle a$ is complementary with an angle whose measure is 45°, then what is the measure of $\angle x$?

Axioms and Figures

EXAMPLE   Axiom 4   Things that are alike or coincide with one another are equal to one another.

Axiom 5   The whole, or sum, is greater than the parts.

Directions   Answer each question. Tell which axiom you used.

1. These two figures are both complete circles with radii of 1 inch. What can you say about the two circles? Why?

_____

_____

2. This rectangle measures 1 inch long and 2 inches wide. If you were to cut it in half along the dotted line, what could you say about the two halves that would be created? Why?

_____

_____

3. These two triangles each have three sides that measure 1 inch and interior angles that measure 60°. What could you say about the two triangles? Why?

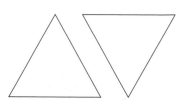

_____

_____

4. Which angles are less than 180°? Why?

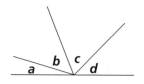

_____

_____

5. If you put this equilateral triangle on top of this circle so that the circle's center was of an equal distance from each of the triangle's corners, what could you say about the shapes created using the triangle's corners and the circle's edge? Why?

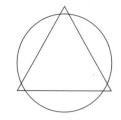

_____

_____

Theorems

EXAMPLE   Review the theorem proving that vertical angles are equal.

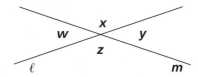

Statement	**Reason**
1. Lines ℓ and m intersect to form vertical $\angle x$ and $\angle y$.	1. Given.
2. $m\angle x + m\angle y = 180°$	2. $\angle x$ and $\angle y$ are adjacent on ℓ and are supplementary.
3. $m\angle w + m\angle z = 180°$	3. $\angle w$ and $\angle z$ are adjacent on ℓ and are supplementary.
4. $m\angle x + m\angle y = m\angle w + m\angle z$	4. Axiom 1, substitution, and Steps 2 and 3.
5. $\therefore m\angle x = m\angle z$	5. Axiom 3. If equals are subtracted from equals, the differences are equal.

Directions   Use the vertical angle theorem to find the measures of angles x, y, and z. List each step and the reason for each step.

1.

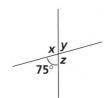

2.

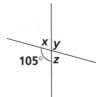

3.

4.

5.

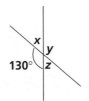

Reasoning

EXAMPLE   List as many reasons as you can that prove that all four angles
are right angles.
1. Vertical angles are equal.
2. Postulate 4, right angles are equal.
3. Each of the adjacent angles to the measured right angle must
also be a right angle because the adjacent angles are supplementary.
Therefore, the vertical angle must also be a right angle because
it is adjacent and supplementary to those angles.

Directions   Give a reason for each of the following statements.
Use the diagram below.

Given: line ℓ intersects line m

1. $m\angle w = m\angle y$

2. $m\angle w < 180°$

3. $m\angle y < 180°$

4. $180° - m\angle w = 180° - m\angle y$

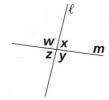

Directions   Give two different reasons for each of the following statements.
Use the diagram below.

5. $m\angle a = m\angle c$

6. $m\angle b = m\angle d$

7. $m\angle a = m\angle b = m\angle c = m\angle d$

8. $m\angle a - m\angle c = m\angle b - m\angle d$

Art and Geometry

EXAMPLE This construction uses one
repeated shape to create
an artistic pattern.

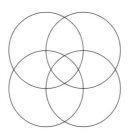

Directions Draw the initial shape on a separate piece of paper and cut the shape out.
Then use the cutout shape to trace the following constructions.

1. Use a circle as a pattern. Start with two circles
whose edges just touch. Then draw a third so
that its edges just touch the edges of the other
two. Continue draw-
ing circles in this
manner until you
create a larger shape
such as a triangle or a
hexagon.

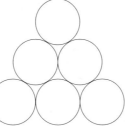

2. Use an equilateral
triangle with 1-
centimeter sides as a
pattern. Stack the
triangles so that their
sides coincide.
Continue placing
triangles next to each
other until you create a larger shape.

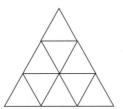

3. Use a square with 1-centimeter sides as a
pattern. Stack the squares in rows to create a
larger shape.

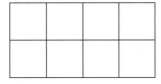

4. Turn the square on end to form another
pattern. Place the squares side by side.

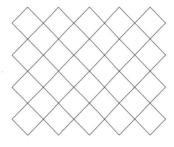

5. Use all three shapes to create a pattern all
your own. Feel free to experiment with
different sequences of the three shapes.

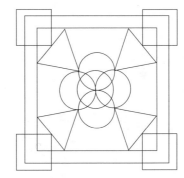

Figures with Parallel Lines

EXAMPLE   Parallel lines are coplanar lines
that never meet.

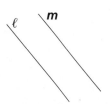

Skew lines are noncoplanar lines
that never meet.

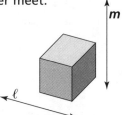

Directions   Look at each figure. Find all of the parallel lines and trace them in red.
Find all of the nonparallel lines and trace them in green.

1.

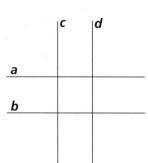

2.

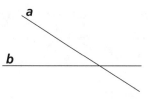

3.

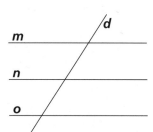

4.

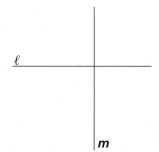

5.

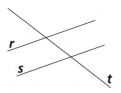

More Figures with Parallel Lines

EXAMPLE   This cube has 12 sets of parallel lines.

Directions   State how many pairs of lines are parallel in each situation.

1.

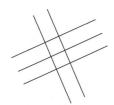

2.

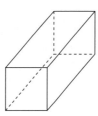

3.

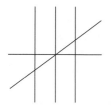

4.

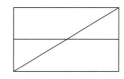

Directions   Answer the following question.

5. What do you think the cube in the example would look like if all of the panels were unfolded so that the resulting image could lay flat on a table? Draw a picture to show your answer.

Transversals

EXAMPLE   Line *t* is a transversal that crosses parallel lines ℓ and *m*.

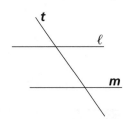

Directions   Name the transversal in each figure.

1.

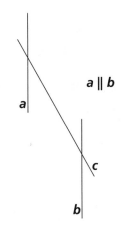

a ∥ *b*

2.

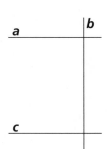

a ∥ *c*

3.

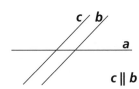

c ∥ *b*

4.

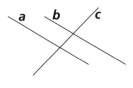

a ∥ *b*

Directions   Construct two parallel lines using the two edges of your straightedge.
Draw a transversal that is not perpendicular to the parallels.
Use a protractor to measure the angles and answer the following questions.

5. Which angles appear to be equal? Which angles appear to be supplementary?

More Transversals

EXAMPLE

A transversal creates eight angles. These angles are categorized as exterior, interior, corresponding, alternate interior, alternate exterior, or supplementary angles.

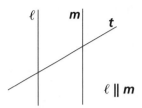

ℓ ‖ m

Directions   Use the figure at the right for problems 1–5.

1. Name the interior angles.

2. Name the exterior angles.

3. Name eight pairs of supplementary angles.

4. Name all pairs of corresponding angles.

5. Name all pairs of alternate interior angles.

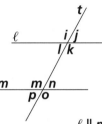

ℓ ‖ m

Directions   Use the figure shown for problems 6–10. Name the angles as *exterior*, *interior*, *alternate exterior*, *alternate interior*, *corresponding*, or *supplementary*.

6. ∠a and ∠e

   _____

7. ∠b and ∠h

   _____

8. ∠d and ∠f

   _____

9. ∠a and ∠d and ∠g and ∠f

   _____

10. ∠c and ∠b and ∠e and ∠h

   _____

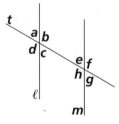

ℓ ‖ m

Theorems Using Parallel Lines

EXAMPLE **Theorem 1:** If two lines are parallel, then the interior angles on the same side of the transversal are supplementary.
Theorem 2: If two lines are parallel, then the corresponding angles are equal.
Theorem 3: If two lines are parallel, then the alternate interior angles are equal.

Directions Complete the following statements.

Use the figure shown and Theorem 1 for problems 1–2.

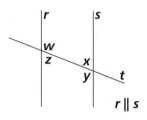

1. $m\angle w + m\angle z =$ _____

2. $m\angle x + m\angle y =$ _____

Use the same figure and Theorem 3 for problems 3–4.

3. $m\angle w =$ _____

4. $m\angle x =$ _____

Use the figure below and Theorem 2 for problems 5–10.

5. $m\angle y =$ _____

6. $m\angle w =$ _____

7. $m\angle t =$ _____

8. $m\angle z =$ _____

9. $m\angle s =$ _____

10. $m\angle u =$ _____

$\ell \parallel m$

Solving Problems with Theorems and Parallel Lines

EXAMPLE   With the three theorems, you can find the measures of all eight angles with the measure of just one.

Since ∠w is a corresponding angle to ∠s, and ∠u is a vertical angle to ∠s, they are both equal to ∠s and measure 60°.
∠t and ∠v are both supplementary to ∠s and therefore measure 120°.
∠y is a vertical angle to ∠w. Therefore, it also measures 60°.
∠x and ∠z are both supplementary to ∠w and therefore measure 120°.

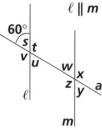

Directions   Find the measures of the angles in the figure. Write your reason for each measure. Use the three theorems about parallel lines and what you know about supplementary and vertical angles.

1. m∠b = _____

2. m∠a = _____

3. m∠c = _____

4. m∠d = _____

5. m∠e = _____

6. m∠f = _____

7. m∠g = _____

8. m∠h = _____

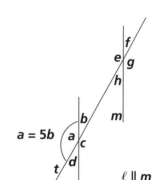

Directions   Solve for x in the following problems.

9. _____

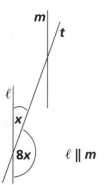

10. _____

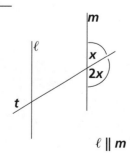

Constructions

EXAMPLE

Given: line *a* and point *X*   •*X*

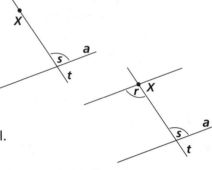

Step 1: Draw a transversal *t* through point *X*.

Step 2: Copy ∠*s* at point *X*. This will produce alternate interior angles that are equal.

Directions For each problem, construct a pair of parallel lines with a set of alternate interior angles that measure *x* degrees. **Hint:** Create the stated angle with one line parallel to the bottom of the page. Place point *X* on the other line and then copy the first angle.

1. $x = 60°$

2. $x = 20°$

3. $x = 100°$

4. $x = 150°$

5. $x = 90°$

6. $x = 75°$

7. $x = 175°$

8. $x = 89°$

9. $x = 5°$

10. $x = 35°$

Quadrilaterals and Parallels

EXAMPLE   A parallelogram is a quadrilateral whose opposite sides are parallel.

A rectangle is a parallelogram with four right angles.

A rhombus is a parallelogram with four equal sides.

A square is a rectangle with sides of equal length.

A trapezoid is a quadrilateral with exactly one pair of parallel sides.

Directions   Use the figure at the right and the definitions and theorems about parallels to complete the following statements.

1. $\overline{AB}$ is parallel to _____.

2. $\overline{AD}$ is parallel to _____.

3. $\overline{AB}$ is not parallel to _____ and _____.

4. $\overline{AD}$ is not parallel to _____ and _____.

5. $\angle 1 + \angle 2 = $ _____

6. $\angle 1 + \angle 4 = $ _____

7. $\angle 2 + \angle 3 = $ _____

8. Angle sum = _____

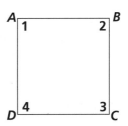

Directions   Use the figure at the right to find the answers.

9. Which sides are parallel? _____

10. $\angle 1 = $ _____

$\angle 1 + \angle 4 = $ _____

Angle sum = _____

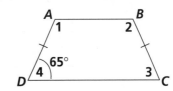

Parallel Lines

EXAMPLE   **Converse 1:** If alternate interior angles are equal, then the lines are parallel. (Postulate)

        Converse 2: If corresponding angles are equal, then the lines are parallel. (Theorem)

        Converse 3: If the sum of the interior angles on the same side of the transversal is 180°, then the lines are parallel. (Theorem)

Directions   Use the diagram shown. Tell which converse you can use to prove that line x is parallel with line y if the angles have the given values.

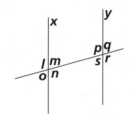

1. $m\angle q = m\angle m$ _____

2. $m\angle p = m\angle n$ _____

3. $m\angle m + m\angle p = 180°$ _____

4. $m\angle r = m\angle n$ _____

5. $m\angle l = m\angle p$ _____

6. $m\angle n + m\angle s = 180°$ _____

7. $m\angle s = m\angle o$ _____

8. $m\angle m = m\angle s$ _____

9. $m\angle s = 75°, m\angle n = 105°$ _____

10. $m\angle l = 35°, m\angle p = 35°$ _____

Polygons

ABCDEF is a polygon. Each segment intersects two others, one at each endpoint.

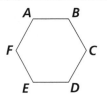

This figure is not a polygon.
Its segments intersect
at points other than their endpoints.

This figure is also not a polygon. Its segments intersect
more than two other segments.

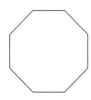

Directions   Write *polygon* or *not a polygon* for each of the figures.
Give reasons why you think any figure is not a polygon.

1.

2.

3.

_____   _____   _____

4.

5.

6.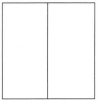

_____   _____   _____

7.

8.

9.

_____   _____   _____

10.

_____

Graphing Ordered Pairs

| EXAMPLE | Graph this point on the coordinate plane.
Point *X* (4, –2) |

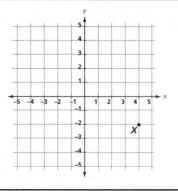

Directions Graph these points on the coordinate plane.

1. *A* (0, 4)

2. *B* (3, –1)

3. *C* (5, 2)

4. *D* (–3, 4)

5. *E* (–4, –1)

6. *F* (4, –5)

7. *G* (–1, –4)

8. *H* (2, –4)

9. *I* (3, 0)

10. *J* (0, 5)

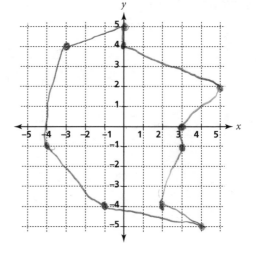

11. *K* (5, 5)

12. *L* (–5, 1)

13. *M* (5, 0)

14. *N* (3, 3)

15. *O* (–2, –2)

16. *P* (–4, 4)

17. *Q* (1, –5)

18. *R* (0, 0)

19. *S* (2, –2)

20. *T* (1, 1)

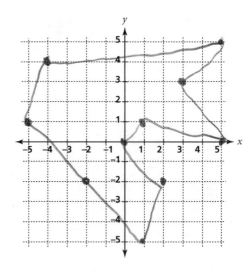

Using Formulas to Graph Ordered Pairs

EXAMPLE   Given the algebraic equation $y = 2x + 3$, graph the
ordered pair of (x, y) when $x = 1$.

If $x = 1$, then $y = 2(1) + 3 = 2 + 3 = 5$.
So the ordered pair is (1, 5).

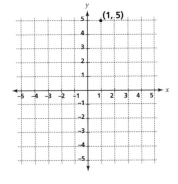

Directions   Use the following equations to find the x- or y-value that is not given.
Graph the ordered pairs on the coordinate plane below.

$y = x - 2$

1. $x = 3$ ___(3, 1)___

2. $x = 5$ ___(5, 3)___

3. $y = 0$ ___(2, 0)___

4. $x = -3$ ___(-3, -5)___

5. $y = -4$ ___(-2, 4)___

$y = 3x$

6. $x = 2$ ___(2, 6)___

7. $y = 3$ ___(1, 3)___

8. $x = -3$ ___(-3, 9)___

9. $y = -6$ ___(-2, -6)___

10. $x = 0$ ___(0, 0)___

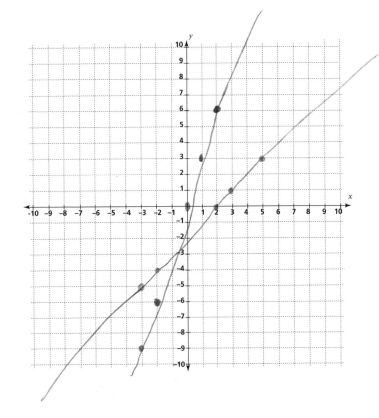

Graphing Horizontal Lines

EXAMPLE   Graph this line.

$y = 2$ and x is any real number

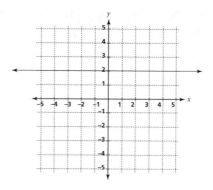

Directions   Draw a graph of each line.

1. $y = 3$ and x is any real number

2. $y = -1$ and x is any real number

3. $y = 4$ and x is any real number

4. $y = -2$ and x is any real number

5. $y = -5$ and x is any real number

6. $y = 0$ and x is any real number

7. $y = 2$ and x is any real number

8. $y = -3$ and x is any real number

9. $y = 5$ and x is any real number

10. $y = -4$ and x is any real number

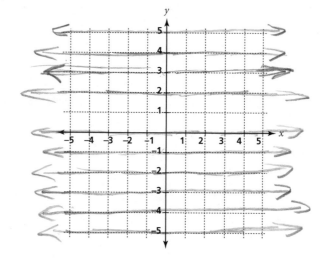

Graphing Ordered Pairs

EXAMPLE   Draw a graph of this line.

(x, 3) where x is any real number

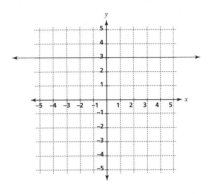

Directions   Draw a graph of each line.

1. (x, −3) where x is any real number
2. (x, 1) where x is any real number
3. (x, −2) where x is any real number
4. (x, 5) where x is any real number
5. (x, −4) where x is any real number
6. (x, 0) where x is any real number
7. (x, −5) where x is any real number
8. (x, 2) where x is any real number
9. (x, 4) where x is any real number
10. (x, −1) where x is any real number

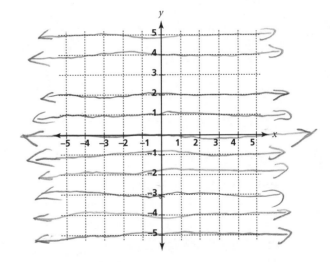

Graphing Vertical Lines

| EXAMPLE | Draw a graph of this line. |

$x = 1$ and y is any real number

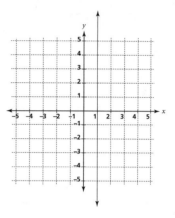

Directions   Draw a graph of each line.

1. $x = -2$ and y is any real number

2. $x = -1$ and y is any real number

3. $x = 3$ and y is any real number

4. $x = -4$ and y is any real number

5. $x = 5$ and y is any real number

6. $x = 0$ and y is any real number

7. $x = 2$ and y is any real number

8. $x = -5$ and y is any real number

9. $x = -3$ and y is any real number

10. $x = 4$ and y is any real number

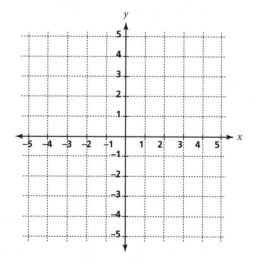

Graphing Ordered Pairs

Draw a graph of this line.

(–4, *y*) where *y* is any real number

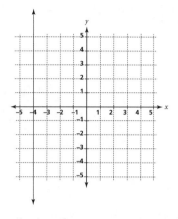

Directions Draw a graph of each line.

1. (4, *y*) where *y* is any real number

2. (1, *y*) where *y* is any real number

3. (2, *y*) where *y* is any real number

4. (–5, *y*) where *y* is any real number

5. (3, *y*) where *y* is any real number

6. (0, *y*) where *y* is any real number

7. (–2, *y*) where *y* is any real number

8. (–1, *y*) where *y* is any real number

9. (5, *y*) where *y* is any real number

10. (–3, *y*) where *y* is any real number

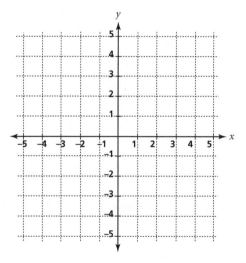

Finding the Slope of a Line

EXAMPLE Find the slope, *m*, of a line that passes through these points.

(0, 0) and (6, 3)

The formula for finding the slope of a line is $\frac{y_1 - y_2}{x_1 - x_2} = m$.

Put the given points into the formula: $\frac{0 - 3}{0 - 6} = \frac{-3}{-6} = \frac{1}{2}$.

The slope is $\frac{1}{2}$.

Directions Find the slope of the line that passes through the given points.

1. $(-2, 5)$ and $(4, 0)$ _____

2. $(0, 3)$ and $(-2, 4)$ _____

3. $(-3, 4)$ and $(-5, 6)$ _____

4. $(3, -2)$ and $(4, 0)$ _____

5. $(5, 5)$ and $(3, 1)$ _____

6. $(-2, -1)$ and $(-3, 1)$ _____

7. $(-4, -3)$ and $(4, 1)$ _____

8. $(2, -1)$ and $(2, 5)$ _____

9. $(0, 2)$ and $(1, 7)$ _____

10. $(3, 3)$ and $(-3, 0)$ _____

11. $(0, 0)$ and $(3, 3)$ _____

12. $(-4, 2)$ and $(4, 2)$ _____

13. $(-3, 5)$ and $(-2, 0)$ _____

14. $(2, 2)$ and $(-3, -3)$ _____

15. $(-4, 3)$ and $(-5, 6)$ _____

The Slope of Parallel Lines

EXAMPLE   Find the slope for this pair of lines.
The formula for finding the slope of a line is $\frac{y_1 - y_2}{x_1 - x_2} = m$.

Put the given points into the formula:

line ℓ $\frac{0-3}{3-0} = \frac{-3}{3} = -1$

line m $\frac{0-(-3)}{-3-0} = \frac{3}{-3} = -1$

The slope formula shows that both line ℓ and line m have a slope of −1.

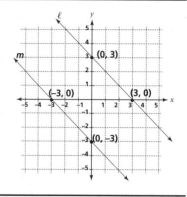

Directions   Find the slope for each pair of lines.

1.

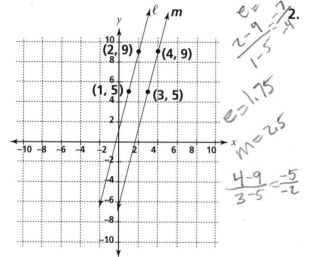

$\frac{2-9}{1-5} = \frac{-7}{-4}$ $e=1.75$

$m=2.5$ $\frac{4-9}{3-5} = \frac{-5}{-2}$

2.

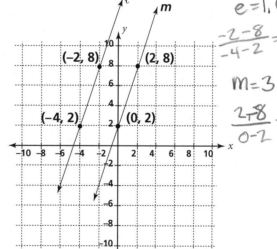

$e=1.67$ $\frac{-2-8}{-4-2} = \frac{-10}{-6}$

$m=3$ $\frac{2-8}{0-2} = \frac{-6}{-2}$

3.

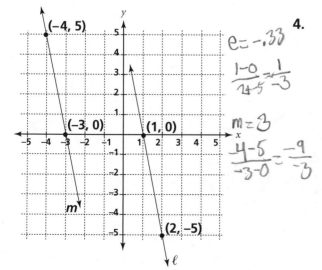

$e=-.33$ $\frac{1-0}{1+5} = \frac{1}{-3}$ $m=3$ $\frac{4-5}{-3-0} = \frac{-9}{-3}$

4.

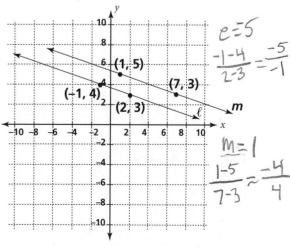

$e=5$ $\frac{-1-4}{2-3} = \frac{-5}{-1}$ $m=1$ $\frac{1-5}{7-3} = \frac{-4}{4}$

Geometry

$y = mx + b$

EXAMPLE Write the equation of line ℓ. Use the form $y = mx + b$.

The slope formula shows that $\frac{y_1 - y_2}{x_1 - x_2} = \frac{4 - 2}{4 - 3} = \frac{2}{1} = 2 = m$.

To solve for b, put one point's x- and y-values plus the value for m into the formula $y = mx + b$.

Using the first point, $2 = 2(3) + b$; $2 = 6 + b$; $b = -4$.

The equation is written as $y = 2x - 4$.

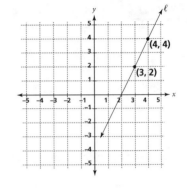

Directions Write the equation of line ℓ. Use the form $y = mx + b$.

1.

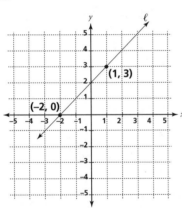

2.

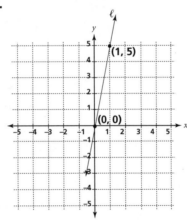

3.

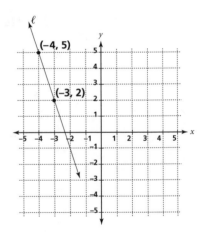

4.

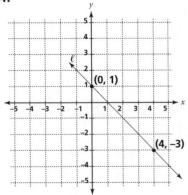

5.

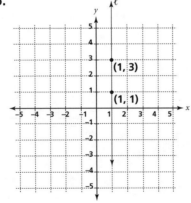

Using Slope in Real-Life Examples

EXAMPLE A staircase has 10 stairs that are 8 inches high and 12 inches deep. If the base of the staircase is at (0, 0), what are the staircase's domain, range, and slope? What would the ordered pair for the top of the staircase be if the numbers were counted in inches?

The domain of the staircase is 108 inches. Because the depth of the last stair is actually part of the second floor, the domain is the depth of each stair, or 12 times the nine stairs that have depth, giving 108 inches.

The range of the staircase is 80 inches—the number of stairs (10) times the height of each stair (8).

The slope of the staircase is $\frac{2}{3}$.

The ordered pair for the top of the staircase is (108, 80).

Directions Solve the following problems.

A surveyor finds that a nearby hill's crest has a horizontal distance of 300 feet from the spot where she is standing. The elevation of the hill's crest is 100 feet.

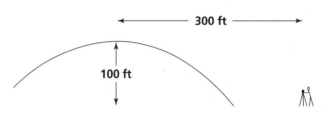

1. What are the domain, range, and slope of the hill from where she is standing? _____

A diagonal is drawn from opposite corners of a rectangle. The rectangle is standing on one of its shorter sides, which is 4 inches, and the slope of the diagonal is 2.

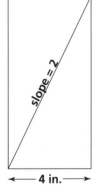

2. What is the length of the two longer sides? _____

3. What are the domain and range of the diagonal? _____

A seesaw has a horizontal distance of 10 feet from one seat to the other. The vertical distance of the seat not resting on the ground is 4 feet.

4. What are the domain, range, and slope of the seesaw? _____

5. Write an equation for each problem.

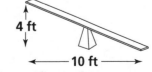

hill _____

diagonal _____

seesaw _____

The Point-Slope Formula

Graph this line using the slope
and point given.

Line ℓ $m = 2$, passes through (3, 4)

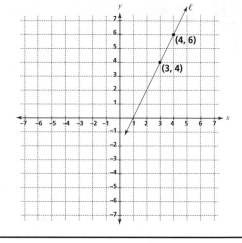

Directions   Graph each line using the slope
and point given.

1. Line a; $m = \frac{1}{2}$, passes through (2, −1)

2. Line b; $m = -2$, passes through (0, −3)

3. Line c; $m = -\frac{3}{4}$, passes through (3, 5)

4. Line d; $m = 3$, passes through (−5, 1)

5. Line e; $m = \frac{5}{2}$, passes through (2, 0)

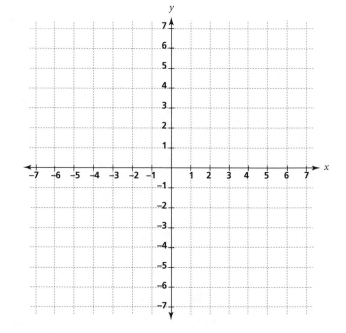

Directions   Write the equation for each line
you graphed in problems 1–5.

6. Line a _____

7. Line b _____

8. Line c _____

9. Line d _____

10. Line e _____

More Point-Slope

Graph this line using the slope
and point given.

Line ℓ $m = -\frac{1}{6}$, passes through (–2, 5)

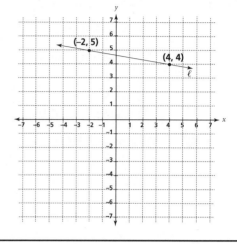

Directions Graph each line using the slope
and point given.

1. Line a; $m = -\frac{5}{4}$, passes through (–3, –2)

2. Line b; $m = 3$, passes through (0, 0)

3. Line c; $m = -4$, passes through (–5, 5)

4. Line d; $m = \frac{3}{7}$, passes through (–2, –4)

5. Line e; $m = -\frac{3}{2}$, passes through (1, 1)

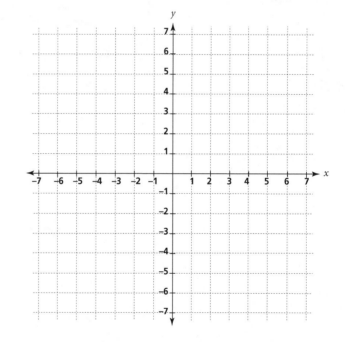

Directions Write the equation for each line
you graphed in problems 1–5.

6. Line a _____

7. Line b _____

8. Line c _____

9. Line d _____

10. Line e _____

The Midpoint of a Segment

EXAMPLE

Review the midpoint formula.

$\frac{x_1 + x_2}{2}$ = midpoint *x*-value

$\frac{y_1 + y_2}{2}$ = midpoint *y*-value

$\frac{6 + 0}{2} = \frac{6}{2} = 3$ = midpoint *x*-value

$\frac{4 + 0}{2} = \frac{4}{2} = 2$ = midpoint *y*-value

The midpoint of the line segment is (3, 2).

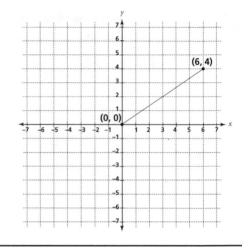

Directions   Find the midpoints of the following line segments.
Be sure to give both coordinates of each midpoint.

1.
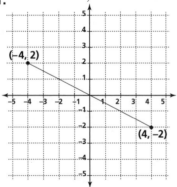

2.
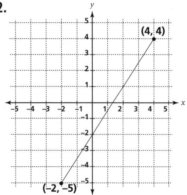

3.
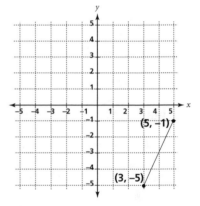

4.
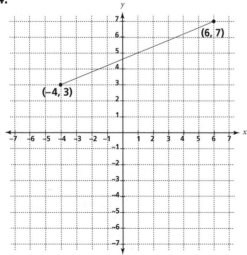

5.
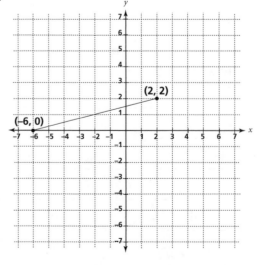

Graphing Line Segments

EXAMPLE   Use the point and the midpoint given to find the other endpoint of the line segment.

   (0, 0) is the first endpoint of the line segment.

   (3, 3) is the midpoint of the line segment.

Using the midpoint formula, you can solve for the line segment's other endpoint.

   $(x_1, y_1) = (0, 0)$, midpoint x-value = 3, midpoint y-value = 3

   $\frac{0 + x_2}{2} = 3$; $\frac{x_2}{2} = 3$; multiply each side by 2; $x_2 = 6$

   $\frac{0 + y_2}{2} = 3$; $\frac{y_2}{2} = 3$; multiply each side by 2; $y_2 = 6$

   The other endpoint is at (6, 6).

Directions   Find the second endpoint for each line segment using the given endpoint and midpoint. Then graph the line segment with both endpoints and midpoint on a coordinate plane.

1. Endpoint = (4, 6); midpoint = (2, 0) _____

2. Endpoint = (−3, −5); midpoint = (−1, −1) _____

3. Endpoint = (5, 4); midpoint = (3, 1) _____

4. Endpoint = (3, −5); midpoint = (−1, −2) _____

5. Endpoint = (−2, 6); midpoint = (1, 1) _____

6. Endpoint = (−5, −3); midpoint = (−4, −2) _____

7. Endpoint = (4, 4); midpoint = (5, −2) _____

8. Endpoint = (1, 7); midpoint = (3, 2) _____

9. Endpoint = (−3, −4); midpoint = (1, −1) _____

10. Endpoint = (1, 1); midpoint = (2, 0) _____

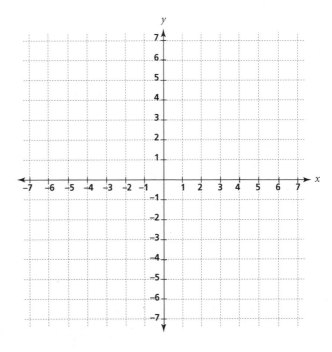

Water Slides

| EXAMPLE | Like a roller coaster, a water slide is a ride that uses slope to create its thrill. Calculate the slope of the first drop in this water slide. |

The height of the starting point is 90 feet.
The height of the end of the first drop is 60 feet.
The horizontal distance covered
in the first drop is 60 feet.
Rise = height of start – height of first drop
$= 90 - 60 = 30$ feet
Run = horizontal distance covered = 60 feet
Slope $= \frac{30}{60} = \frac{1}{2}$

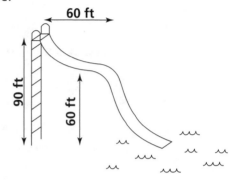

Directions   Find the slope of each section of the following water slides.

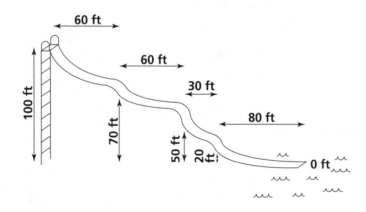

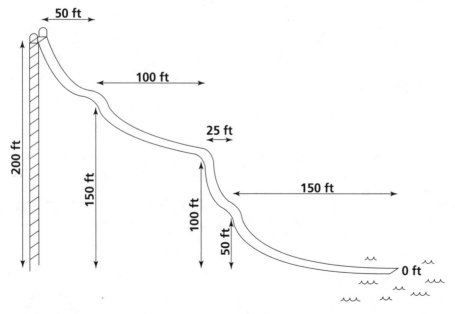

Triangle Sides

EXAMPLE	Equilateral triangles have three equal sides.

Isosceles triangles have two equal sides.

Scalene triangles have no equal sides.

Is a triangle with the following side lengths an equilateral, isosceles, or scalene triangle?

Q. Triangle *ABC* has sides that measure 8, 9, and 9 units.

A. Triangle *ABC* is an isosceles triangle.

Directions   Identify each triangle as *equilateral, isosceles,* or *scalene.*

1. Triangle *ABC* has sides that measure 3, 3, and 3 units in length. _____

2. Triangle *EFG* has sides that measure 9, 17, and 14 units in length. _____

3. Triangle *HIJ* has sides that measure 4, 4, and 7 units in length. _____

4. Triangle *KLM* has sides that measure 8, 10, and 8 units in length. _____

5. Triangle *NOP* has sides that measure 8, 9, and 11 units in length. _____

6. Triangle *QRS* has sides that measure 8, 8, and 8 units in length. _____

7. Triangle *TUV* has sides that measure 2, 3, and 4 units in length. _____

8. Triangle *WXY* has sides that measure 19, 19, and 30 units in length. _____

9. Triangle *DZA* has sides that measure 7.5, 7.5, and 7.5 units in length. _____

10. Triangle *BTU* has sides that measure 6, 7, and 10 units in length. _____

11. Line segment *AB* in triangle *ABC* is equal to line segment *AC*
and four times the length of line segment *BC*. _____

12. Line segment *DE* in triangle *DEF* is equal to line segment *EF*
and line segment *DF*. _____

13. Line segment *XY* in triangle *XYZ* is not equal to either line
segment *YZ* or *XZ*. _____

14. Line segment *WX* in triangle *WXY* is equal to line segment *XY* and
not congruent to line segment *YW*. _____

15. Line segment *XY* in triangle *XYZ* is equal to line segments
YZ and *XZ*. _____

Naming Triangles by Their Angles

EXAMPLE	Acute triangles have three angles less than 90°.
	Obtuse triangles have one obtuse angle.
	Right triangles have one right angle.
	Equilateral triangles have three equal angles.
	Isosceles triangles have two equal angles.
	Scalene triangles have no equal angles.

Directions   Name each of these triangles using its angles.

1. Triangle *ABC* has angles that measure 100°, 40°, and 40°.   _____

2. Triangle *DEF* has angles that measure 60°, 70°, and 50°.   _____

3. Triangle *GHI* has angles that measure 60°, 60°, and 60°.   _____

4. Triangle *JKL* has angles that measure 110°, 30°, and 40°.   _____

5. Triangle *MNO* has angles that measure 90°, 45°, and 45°.   _____

6. Triangle *PQR* has angles that measure 90°, 40°, and 50°.   _____

7. Triangle *STU* has angles that measure 80°, 50°, and 50°.   _____

8. Triangle *VWX* has angles that measure 130°, 30°, and 20°.   _____

9. ∠*BAC* in triangle *ABC* measures 60° and is equal to ∠*ABC*.   _____

10. ∠*BAC* in triangle *ABC* measures 90°, and ∠*ABC* and ∠*BCA* are not equal to each other.   _____

Constructing Triangles Using Their Angles

EXAMPLE   Construct △ABC with ∠CAB = 2∠BCA and
m∠B = 90°.

Step 1 Draw a right angle. Label it ∠B.

Step 2 Pick a point along one of the rays of ∠B. Label this point A.
Using your protractor, draw an angle that measures 30° using
point A as the vertex and one ray of ∠B as one side. Extend
the new ray so that it crosses the other ray of ∠B. Label the
point where it crosses, point C.

Step 3 Measure ∠ACB. It should measure 60°. You have now
constructed a right triangle with acute angles that have a ratio
of 2 to 1. This triangle is a type of right scalene triangle.

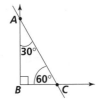

Directions Complete the following constructions. Use a separate sheet
of paper. You will need a straightedge and a protractor.

1. Construct an isosceles triangle in which the sum of its two
    equal angles equals the measure of its third angle.

2. Construct an isosceles triangle in which the sum of its two
    equal angles is equal to $\frac{1}{2}$ the measure of its third angle.

3. Construct a scalene triangle that has a right angle and two
    other angles with a ratio of 8 to 1.

4. Construct an equilateral triangle by drawing one 60° angle
    and then another 60° angle off one of the first angle's rays.

5. Construct an isosceles triangle in which the sum of its two
    equal angles is equal to twice the measure of its third angle.

Special Quadrilaterals

EXAMPLE   Identify whether a quadrilateral with the following parameters is possible.

Figure *ABCD* has four sides. Side *AB* is equal to side *CD*. ∠*DAB* and ∠*DCB* are right angles.

Solution: Figure *ABCD* is either a square or a rectangle.

Directions   Is a quadrilateral with the following parameters possible? Write *True* if it can exist or *False* if it cannot exist. If the figure can exist, identify which type of quadrilateral the figure is.

1. Figure *ABCD* has four sides that are equal. Two of its angles each measure 70° and the other two angles each measure 110°.   _____

2. Figure *ABCD* has four sides. $\overline{CD}$ is twice the length of $\overline{AB}$. ∠*ADC* and ∠*DCB* both measure 60°.   _____

3. Figure *ABCD* has four sides that are equal. Three of its angles each measure 85° and the fourth angle measures 95°.   _____

4. Figure *ABCD* has four sides that are not equal. The measures of its angles are 88°, 89°, 91°, and 92°.   _____

5. Figure *ABCD* has four sides. Three of these sides are of equal length. The fourth side is twice the length of any of the other sides. The figure also has two sets of equal angles.   _____

6. Figure *ABCD* has four sides. These sides are two pairs of equal lengths, neither of which is equal to the other pair's length. The figure also has two pairs of equal angles, neither of which is equal to the other pair's measure.   _____

7. Figure *ABCD* has four sides. Two of these sides are parallel. Two of the figure's angles are right angles. The other two angles are not right angles.   _____

8. Figure *ABCD* has four sides. The figure has two pairs of equal sides, neither of which is equal to the other. The figure has two equal angles and one angle that is larger than 180°.   _____

9. Figure *ABCD* has four sides that are equal. The figure's angles measure 87°, 87°, 93°, and 91°.   _____

10. Figure *ABCD* has four sides that are not equal. The figure has four angles that are equal.   _____

Diagonals

 EXAMPLE   Review the following proof.

Given: *ABCD* is a square, $\overline{AC}$ is a diagonal, and m∠1 = 45°.

Problem: Find the measures of ∠2, ∠3, ∠4.

Statement	Reason
1. ∠1 = 45°	1. Given.
2. ∠C is a right angle.	2. Given: definition of a square.
3. ∠1 + ∠2 = 90° and 45° + ∠2 = 90°	3. Substitution of equals.
4. ∠2 = 45°	4. Subtraction of equals.
5. $\overline{BC}$ is parallel to $\overline{AD}$ and $\overline{AC}$ is a transversal.	5. Given: definition of a square and transversal.
6. Therefore, ∠4 = ∠1 = 45°	6. Alternate interior angles.
7. $\overline{AB}$ is parallel to $\overline{DC}$ and $\overline{AC}$ is a transversal.	7. Given: definition of a square and transversal.
8. Therefore, ∠2 = ∠3 = 45°	8. Alternate interior angles.

You have proven that angles 1, 2, 3, and 4 each measure 45°.

Directions   Complete the problems. Write the missing reasons.

Given: *WXYZ* is a rectangle, $\overline{WY}$ is a diagonal.
Problem: Show that ∠1 ≅ ∠3 and ∠2 ≅ ∠4.

1. $\overline{XY}$ is parallel to $\overline{WZ}$.   **1.** _____

2. ∠1 = ∠3   **2.** _____

3. $\overline{WX}$ is parallel to $\overline{ZY}$.   **3.** _____

4. ∠2 = ∠4   **4.** _____

Given: for the above rectangle *WXYZ*, ∠1 is five times the measure of ∠2.
Problem: Find the measures of ∠1 and ∠2.

5. ∠Y is a right angle.   **5.** _____

6. ∠1 + ∠2 = 90°   **6.** _____

7. ∠2 = 15°   **7.** _____

8. ∠1 = 75°   **8.** _____

Given: *WXYZ* is a parallelogram with diagonal *WY*.
Problem: Show that ∠1 ≅ ∠3.

9. $\overline{XY}$ is parallel to $\overline{WZ}$.   **9.** _____

10. ∠1 = ∠3   **10.** _____

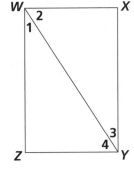

More Diagonals

EXAMPLE **Given:** *WXYZ* is a rectangle with diagonal *WY* and m∠1 is four times as large as ∠2.
Problem: Find the measures of ∠1, ∠2, ∠3, and ∠4.

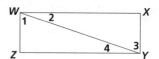

Solution
∠Y is a right angle. ∠1 + ∠2 = 90°
Find the m∠1 and m∠2.   4x(∠1) + x(∠2) = 90°   5x = 90°   x = 18°
   ∠2 = 18°
   ∠1 = 72°
Find the m∠3 and m∠4.
   ∠1 = ∠3   alternate interior angles
   ∠2 = ∠4   alternate interior angles

∠1 and ∠3 = 72° and ∠2 and ∠4 = 18°

Directions Find the measures of the angles.

Given: *EFGH* is a rectangle with diagonal *EG* and ∠3 is eight times as large as ∠4.

1. m∠1 = _____
2. m∠2 = _____
3. m∠3 = _____
4. m∠4 = _____

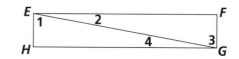

Given: *JKLM* is a rectangle with diagonal *JL* and ∠1 is twice as large as ∠2.

5. m∠1 = _____
6. m∠2 = _____
7. m∠3 = _____
8. m∠4 = _____

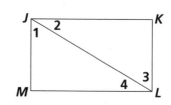

Given: *MNOP* is a rectangle with diagonal *MO* and ∠3 is seventeen times as large as ∠4.

9. m∠1 = _____
10. m∠2 = _____

Triangle Angles

EXAMPLE

Find the measure of ∠x.

The angle sum of any triangle is 180°.

You are given the measures of two angles (the 90° right angle and the 55° angle) and are asked to find the measure of the third.

You can write the equation 180° = 90° + 55° + x. This can be reduced to 180° = 145° + x. Subtract 145° from both sides to get x = 35°.

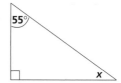

Directions Find the measure of ∠x.

1.
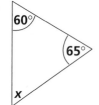
_____

2.
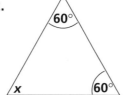
_____

3.
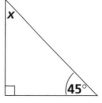
_____

4.

_____

5.

_____

6.
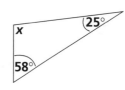
_____

7.
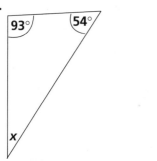
_____

8.
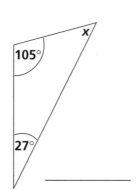
_____

9.
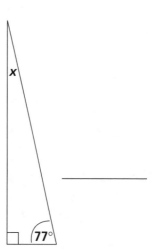
_____

10.
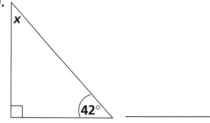
_____

Triangle Angles and Algebra

EXAMPLE   Find the value of *x*.

You know that all triangles have angle measures that total 180°.

You are given the measure of one angle and variable measures for the other two angles. You can write the equation 180° = 90° + *x* + *x*. This can be reduced to 180° = 90° + 2*x*. Subtract 90° from both sides to get 90° = 2*x*. Divide both sides by 2 to get *x* = 45°.

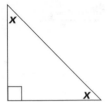

Directions   Find the value of *x*.

1.

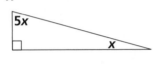

_____

2.

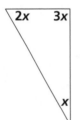

_____

3.

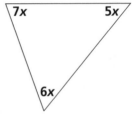

_____

4.

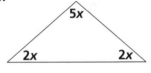

_____

5.

_____

6.

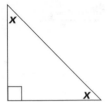

_____

7.

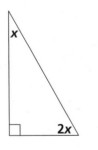

_____

8.

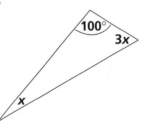

_____

9.

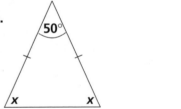

_____

10.

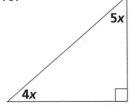

_____

Constructing Regular Polygons

EXAMPLE   Construct a regular pentagon using $\overline{XY}$ as the length of the sides.

Calculate the measure of the pentagon's interior angles. The degrees in a polygon can be found using the formula $(n - 2) \cdot (180°)$ where n is the number of sides the polygon has. Write the equation $(5 - 2) \cdot (180°)$. Calculate $3 \cdot 180° = 540°$. A pentagon has five interior angles. Find out the measure of each angle in a regular pentagon by dividing the total number of degrees by the number of equal interior angles. $\frac{540}{5} = 108$. Each angle of a regular pentagon $= 108°$.

Step 1   Using a protractor, draw an angle that measures 108°. Label the vertex point A.

Step 2   Open your compass to match $\overline{XY}$. Using point A as the center of a circle, draw an arc on both rays of $\angle A$. Label the points where the arcs cross the rays, B and E.

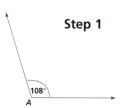

Step 3   Copy $\angle BAE$ at B and extend the new ray. Open the compass to match $\overline{XY}$ and draw an arc on the newest ray. Label the point where the arc crosses the ray, C.

Step 4   Copy $\angle BAE$ at C and extend its new ray. Open the compass to match $\overline{XY}$ and draw an arc on this new ray. Label this point D. Connect D and E to complete the regular pentagon.

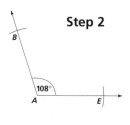

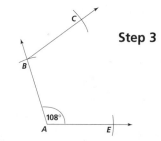

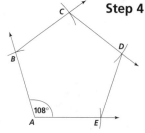

Directions   Do the following constructions on a separate sheet of paper. Use a protractor to draw the first angle and then a straightedge and a compass to complete the polygon.

1. Construct a regular pentagon.

2. Construct a regular octagon.

3. Construct a regular decagon.

4. Construct a regular septagon.

5. Construct a regular hexagon.

Geometric Patterns

EXAMPLE   Use a straightedge to draw all of the possible diagonals from one vertex in this polygon.

 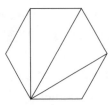

Directions   Draw all of the diagonals from one vertex in each of these polygons.

1.

2.

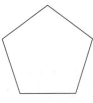

3.

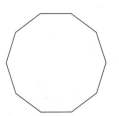

4.

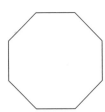

5.

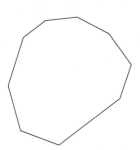

Constructing Perpendiculars

EXAMPLE   Construct a perpendicular to line *m* that passes through point *X*. _____ *m*

Step 1   Open your compass to a distance somewhat greater than the distance from
X to *m*. Using *X* as the center of a circle, draw an arc that intersects *m* in
two places. Label the points *A* and *B*.   *X* •

Step 2   Keeping your compass opening constant, and using *A* as the center of a circle,
draw an arc above *m*. Then, with the same compass opening, draw a second arc
above *m* using *B* as the center. Label the point where the arcs intersect, *C*.

Step 3   Connect *X* and *C*. $\overline{XC}$ is perpendicular to *m*.

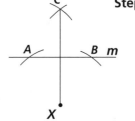

Directions   Do the following constructions on a separate sheet of paper.
Use only a compass and a straightedge.

1. Construct a ⊥ to $\overline{AB}$
that passes through *C*.

2. Construct a ⊥ to $\overline{AB}$
that passes through *D*.

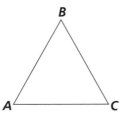

3. Construct a ⊥ to $\overline{AB}$ that
passes through *C*, to $\overline{BC}$
that passes through *A*,
and to $\overline{AC}$ that
passes through *B*.

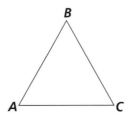

4. Construct a ⊥ to $\overline{AB}$ that
passes through *D*, to $\overline{BC}$
that passes through *E*, to
$\overline{CD}$ that passes through
A, to $\overline{DE}$ that passes
through *B*, and to $\overline{EA}$
that passes through *C*.

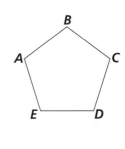

5. Draw a right triangle. Construct a ⊥ from the
right angle to the opposite side.

More Perpendiculars

EXAMPLE Construct a line perpendicular to *m* and through point *X*.

Step 1 Open your compass to any radius. Using *X* as the center of a circle, draw an arc, which intersects *m* in two places. Label the points *A* and *B*.

Step 2 Increase your compass opening slightly, and using *A* and then *B* as the centers, draw intersecting arcs either above or below *m*. Label the point where the arcs intersect, *C*.

Step 3 Draw $\overline{XC}$. $\overline{XC}$ is perpendicular to *m*.

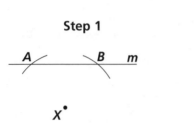

Step 1

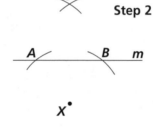

Step 2

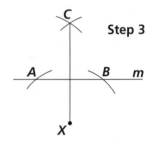

Step 3

Directions Draw perpendiculars to ℓ through all of the points shown. Use a compass and straightedge.

1. point *A*

2. point *B*

3. point *C*

4. point *D*

5. point *E*

6. point *F*

7. point *G*

8. point *H*

9. point *I*

10. point *J*

Angle Bisectors and Medians

EXAMPLE   Angle Bisectors   intersect at the in-center

Medians   intersect at the centroid

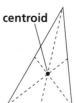

in-center   centroid

Directions   Complete the following constructions. Use a straightedge and a compass.
                    (Note: You may find it easier to use large triangles for your constructions.)

1. Draw any acute triangle and label it *ABC*.
   Construct its angle bisectors and label the in-center.

2. Draw any obtuse triangle and label it *EFG*.
   Construct its angle bisectors and label the in-center.

3. Draw any right triangle and label it *HIJ*.
   Construct its angle bisectors and label the in-center.

4. Draw any acute triangle and label it *KLM*.
   Construct its medians and label the centroid.

5. Draw any obtuse triangle and label it *NOP*.
   Construct its medians and label the centroid.

Altitudes

| EXAMPLE | Altitudes intersect at the orthocenter. |

Acute triangles have altitudes completely
within the triangles.

Obtuse triangles have two exterior altitudes
and one interior altitude.

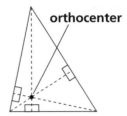
orthocenter

Directions Complete the following constructions. Use a straightedge and a compass.
(Note: You may find it easier to use large triangles for your constructions.)

1. Draw any acute triangle and label it *ABC*.
Construct its altitudes and label the orthocenter.

2. Draw any obtuse triangle and label it *ABC*.
Construct its altitudes and label the orthocenter.

3. Draw any right triangle and label it *ABC*.
Construct its altitudes and label the orthocenter.

Directions Answer the following questions using the given information.

Given: Triangle *ABC*'s largest angle is equal to x.

4. Based on problems 1–3, what can you conclude about
triangle *ABC*'s orthocenter if x is less than 90°? _____

5. What happens to the orthocenter as x increases towards 90°?

_____

What happens to the orthocenter as x reaches 90°?

_____

What happens to the orthocenter as x increases to larger than 90°?

_____

Name _____ Date _____ Period _____

Angle Sum Theorem

EXAMPLE   Use the angle sum theorem or its corollary to find the measures of the angles.

The topmost angle and its two adjacent angles form line ℓ, which is equivalent to a straight angle. Therefore, the sum of the topmost angle and its adjacent angles is equal to 180°. You can solve for *y* by writing the following equation:

$180° = y + y + y$, which can be reduced to $180° = 3y$. Divide both sides by 3 to get $y = 60°$.

The angle sum theorem allows you to solve for *x*. The theorem states that the sum of any triangle's angles must equal 180°. You can write the following equation.

$$180° = y + x + x$$
$$180° = 60° + 2x$$
$$120° = 2x$$

$x = 60°$ You have now found the measures of all three angles in △*ABC*.

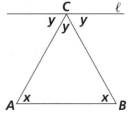

Directions   Use the angle sum theorem or its corollary to find the measures of the angles.

1. Angle *A* _____
2. Angle *B* _____
3. Angle *C* _____

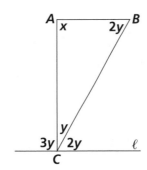

4. Angle *A* _____
5. Angle *B* _____
6. Angle *C* _____

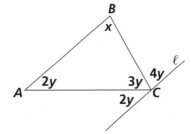

7. Angle *A* _____
8. Angle *B* _____
9. Angle *C* _____
10. ∠*A* + ∠*B* + ∠*C* _____

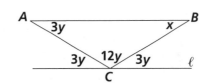

More of the Angle Sum Theorem

EXAMPLE   Use the angle sum theorem or its corollary to find the measures of the angles.

The angle adjacent to ∠C (labeled 2y) is supplementary to ∠C (labeled y). Therefore, the sum of ∠C and the angle labeled 2y is 180°. You can write the following equation to solve for y: 180° = y + 2y. This can be reduced to 180° = 3y. Divide both sides by 3 to get y = 60°.

The angle sum theorem allows you to solve for x. The theorem states that the sum of any triangle's angles must equal 180°. You can write the following equations.

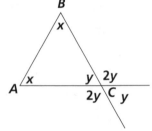

$$180° = y + x + x$$
$$180° = 60° + 2x$$
$$120° = 2x$$
$$x = 60°$$ You have now found the measures of all three angles in △ABC.

Directions   Use the angle sum theorem or its corollary to find the measures of the angles.

1. Angle A _____

2. Angle B _____

3. Angle C _____

4. Angle A _____

5. Angle B _____

6. Angle C _____

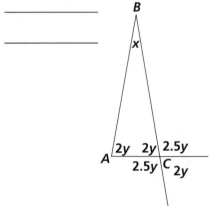

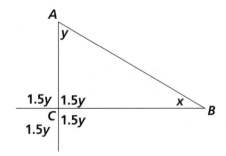

7. Angle A _____

8. Angle B _____

9. Angle C _____

10. ∠A + ∠B + ∠C _____

Geometric Puzzles

EXAMPLE   A tangram puzzle is made from the cut pieces of a square. The following puzzle is made from the cut pieces of an equilateral triangle.

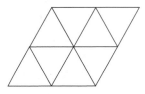

These can be arranged in many ways. For example, a line:

Or a rhombus shape:

Directions   Cut the shapes into the stated number of pieces. As long as all the pieces can be put back together to form the original shape, you may make any kinds of cuts that you want to.

1. Cut this rectangle into five separate pieces and arrange them in at least four different shapes.

4. Cut this circle into seven separate pieces and arrange them in at least four different shapes.

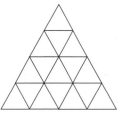

2. Cut this parallelogram into eight separate pieces and arrange them in at least four different shapes.

5. Cut this triangle into four separate pieces and arrange them in at least two different shapes.

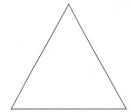

3. Cut this trapezoid into four separate pieces and arrange them in at least four different shapes.

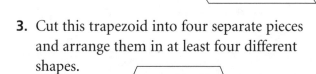

Proving Triangles Congruent by SAS

EXAMPLE   Use the SAS theorem to prove that △ABD and △ACD are congruent.

Given: △ABC is an isosceles triangle with $\overline{AB} = \overline{AC}$.
$\overline{AD}$ is the median and altitude of vertex A.

To Prove: △ABD and △ACD are congruent.

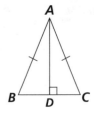

Statement	**Reason**
1. Point D is the midpoint of $\overline{BC}$.	1. Definition of a median.
2. $\overline{BD} = \overline{CD}$	2. Definition of a midpoint.
3. ∠BDA = 90°	3. Definition of an altitude.
4. ∠CDA = 90°	4. Definition of an altitude.
5. ∠BDA = ∠CDA	5. Substitution of equals.
6. $\overline{AD} = \overline{AD}$	6. Any quantity is equal to itself.
7. ∴ △ABD and △ACD are congruent.	7. SAS postulate.

Directions   Copy each proof. Write the reason for each statement.

Given: Figure ABCD is a square with diagonal BD.
To Prove: △ABD ≅ △CBD

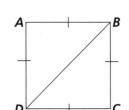

Statement	**Reason**
1. $\overline{AB} = \overline{BC}$	1. _____
2. $\overline{AD} = \overline{DC}$	2. _____
3. ∠A = ∠C	3. _____
4. △ABD ≅ △CBD	4. _____

Given: Figure ABCD is a parallelogram with diagonal BD.
To Prove: △ABD ≅ △CDB

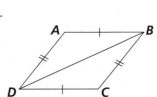

Statement	**Reason**
1. $\overline{AB} = \overline{CD}$	1. _____
2. $\overline{AD} = \overline{CB}$	2. _____
3. $\overline{AB}$ is parallel to $\overline{CD}$.	3. _____
4. ∠ABC + ∠C = 180°	4. _____
5. $\overline{AD}$ is parallel to $\overline{BC}$.	5. _____
6. ∠A + ∠ABC = 180°	6. _____

Finish the proof on a separate sheet of paper with statements and reasons.

Proving Triangles Congruent by SSS

EXAMPLE   Use the SSS postulate to prove given triangles are congruent.

Given: △ABCD is a square with diagonal AC.

To Prove: △ABC ≅ △ADC

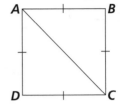

Statement	**Reason**
1. $\overline{AB} = \overline{BC}$	1. Definition of a square.
2. $\overline{AD} = \overline{DC}$	2. Definition of a square.
3. $\overline{AC} = \overline{AC}$	3. Any quantity is equal to itself.
4. △ABC ≅ △ADC	4. SSS postulate.

Directions   Copy each proof. Write the reason for each statement.

Given: Figure ABCD is a parallelogram with diagonal AC.
To Prove: △ABC ≅ △ADC

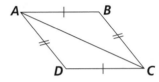

Statement	**Reason**
1. $\overline{AB} = \overline{CD}$	1. _____
2. $\overline{AD} = \overline{BC}$	2. _____
3. $\overline{AC} = \overline{AC}$	3. _____
4. △ABC ≅ △ADC	4. _____

Given: Figure ABC is an isosceles triangle with perpendicular bisector AD.
To Prove: △ABD ≅ △ACD

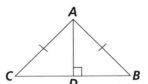

Statement	**Reason**
1. $\overline{AB} = \overline{AC}$	1. _____
2. $\overline{AD} = \overline{AD}$	2. _____
3. $\angle ADB = 90°$	3. _____
4. $\angle ADC = 90°$	4. _____
5. △ABD is a right triangle.	5. _____
6. $\overline{AB}^2 = \overline{AD}^2 + \overline{BD}^2$	6. _____

Finish the proof on a separate sheet of paper with statements and reasons.

Proving Triangles Congruent by ASA

EXAMPLE Prove that the given triangles are congruent using the ASA postulate.

Given: Figure ABC is an isosceles triangle. $\overline{AD}$ bisects ∠A and is perpendicular to $\overline{BC}$.

To Prove: △ABD ≅ △ACD

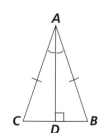

Statement	Reason
1. $\overline{AD}$ bisects ∠A.	1. Given.
2. ∠BAD = ∠CAD	2. Definition of a bisector.
3. $\overline{AD}$ is perpendicular to $\overline{BC}$.	3. Given.
4. ∠ADB = 90°	4. Definition of a perpendicular.
5. ∠ADC = 90°	5. Definition of a perpendicular.
6. ∠ADB = ∠ADC	6. Substitution of equals.
7. $\overline{AD}$ = $\overline{AD}$	7. Any quantity is equal to itself.
8. △ABD ≅ △ACD	8. ASA postulate.

Directions Write the reason for each statement.

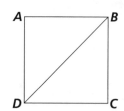

Given: Figure ABCD is a square with diagonal BD.
To Prove: △ABD ≅ △CDB

Statement	Reason
1. $\overline{AB}$ is parallel to $\overline{CD}$.	1. _____
2. $\overline{BD}$ is a transversal of $\overline{AB}$ and $\overline{CD}$.	2. _____
3. ∠ABD = ∠BDC	3. _____
4. $\overline{AD}$ is parallel to $\overline{BC}$.	4. _____
5. $\overline{BD}$ is a transversal of $\overline{AD}$ and $\overline{BC}$.	5. _____
6. ∠ADB = ∠DBC	6. _____
7. $\overline{DB}$ = $\overline{DB}$	7. _____
8. △ABD ≅ △CDB	8. _____

Hypotenuse-Leg Theorem

EXAMPLE   Prove that two triangles are congruent using the Hypotenuse-Leg Theorem.

Given: Figure *ABCD* is a rectangle with diagonal *AC*.

To Prove: $\triangle ABC \cong \triangle ADC$

Statement	Reason
1. $\angle D$ is a right angle.	1. Given: definition of a rectangle.
2. $\angle B$ is a right angle.	2. Definition of a rectangle.
3. $\angle D = \angle B$	3. All right angles are equal with each other.
4. $\overline{AB} = \overline{CD}$	4. Given: definition of a rectangle.
5. $\overline{AC} = \overline{AC}$	5. Any quantity is equal to itself.
6. $\triangle ABC \cong \triangle ADC$	6. H-L Theorem.

Directions   Write the reason for each statement.

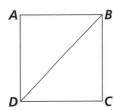

Given: Figure *ABC* is an isosceles triangle with altitude *AD*.

To Prove: $\triangle ABD \cong \triangle ACD$

Statement	Reason
1. $\overline{AB} = \overline{AC}$	1. _____
2. $\overline{AD} = \overline{AD}$	2. _____
3. $\angle ADB$ is a right angle.	3. _____
4. $\angle ADC$ is a right angle.	4. _____
5. $\angle ADB = \angle ADC$	5. _____
6. $\triangle ABD \cong \triangle ACD$	6. _____

Given: Figure *ABCD* is a square with diagonal *BD*.

To Prove: $\triangle ABD \cong \triangle CBD$

Statement	Reason
1. $\overline{AB} = \overline{CD}$	1. _____
2. $\overline{BD} = \overline{BD}$	2. _____
3. $\angle A$ is a right angle.	3. _____
4. $\angle C$ is a right angle.	4. _____

Finish the proof with statements and reasons.

Reflections

EXAMPLE

Reflect the image over the *x*-axis.

Reflected points:

$A' = (0, -2)$

$B' = (5, -2)$

$C' = (3, -5)$

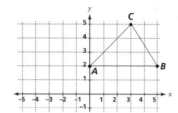

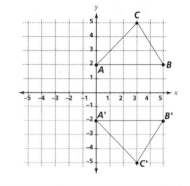

Directions   Reflect each image over the specified axis.
Give the coordinates of the image vertices.

1. Line of reflection = *x*-axis

_____

2. Line of reflection = *y*-axis

_____

3. Line of reflection = *x*-axis

_____

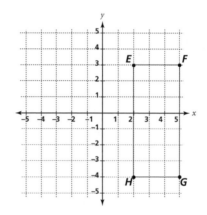

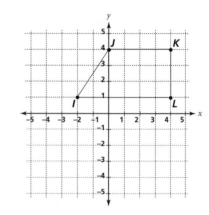

4. Line of reflection = *x*-axis

_____

5. Line of reflection = *y*-axis

_____

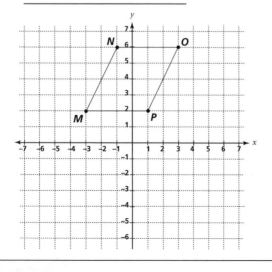

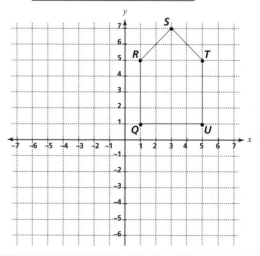

Reflections Over Different Lines

Reflect the image over the specified line of reflection: $x = 2$
Give the coordinates of the image vertices.

Reflected points:

$A' = (1, 3)$

$B' = (-1, 3)$

$C' = (-1, 1)$

$D' = (1, 1)$

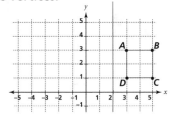

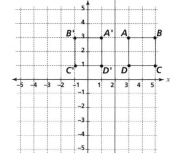

Directions Reflect each image over the specified line of reflection.
Give the coordinates of the image vertices.

1. Line of reflection $x = 3$

_____

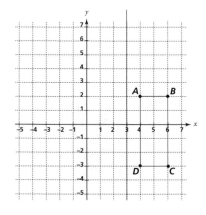

2. Line of reflection $y = 1$

_____

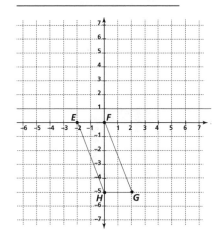

3. Line of reflection $x = -1$

_____

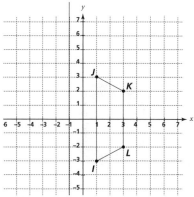

4. Line of reflection $x = 2$

_____

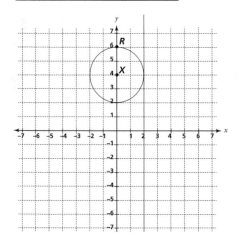

5. Line of reflection $y = -2$

_____

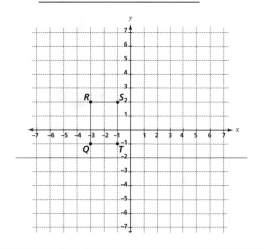

Alphabet Symmetry

EXAMPLE Find the line of symmetry in the letter *A*.

A

The letter *A* has a vertical line of symmetry.

Directions Draw any lines of symmetry that the following letters have.

1.

Y

2.

M

3.

O

4.

B

5.

D

6.

W

7.

X

8.

C

9.

F

10.

H

Identifying Image Translations

EXAMPLE   Name the image point when the object point (3, 4) is mapped
by the following translation.

$$(x, y) \rightarrow (x - 2, y - 5)$$

Image point = (1, –1)

Directions   Name the image point when the object point (4, 4) is mapped
by the following translations.

1. $(x, y) \rightarrow (x - 4, y + 2)$ _____

2. $(x, y) \rightarrow (x + 1, y - 1)$ _____

3. $(x, y) \rightarrow (x - 6, y - 3)$ _____

4. $(x, y) \rightarrow (x + 3, y + 1)$ _____

Directions   Name the image point when the object point (–2, 1) is mapped
by the following translations.

5. $(x, y) \rightarrow (x - 2, y + 1)$ _____

6. $(x, y) \rightarrow (x - 5, y - 1)$ _____

7. $(x, y) \rightarrow (x + 4, y + 3)$ _____

8. $(x, y) \rightarrow (x - 2, y + 3)$ _____

Directions   Name the image point when the object point (–7, 3) is mapped
by the following translations.

9. $(x, y) \rightarrow (x + 24, y - 4)$ _____

10. $(x, y) \rightarrow (x - 1, y - 1)$ _____

11. $(x, y) \rightarrow (x + 5, y - 3)$ _____

12. $(x, y) \rightarrow (x - 3, y + 1)$ _____

Directions   Identify the image of (x, y) under the following translations.
Remember, the image takes the form $(x + a, y + b)$.

13. $(-4, 5) \rightarrow (-6, 2)$ _____

14. $(1, 2) \rightarrow (4, 8)$ _____

15. $(-2, -3) \rightarrow (3, 4)$ _____

Rotating Images

EXAMPLE   Rotate the following image 90° clockwise around point *O*.

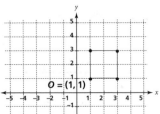

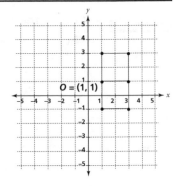

Directions   Copy the given figure onto graph paper. Then rotate the object 90° clockwise around point *O* to produce an image. Draw the image.

1.

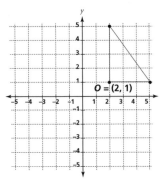

2.

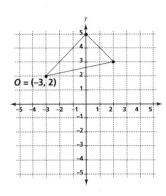

3.

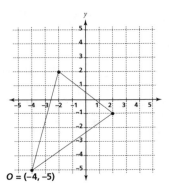

4.

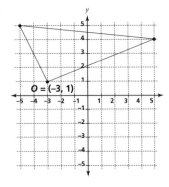

5.

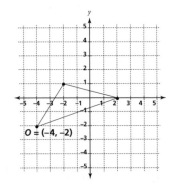

Geometry

Name _____ Date _____ Period _____

Chapter 6

Workbook Activity 71

3-D Symmetry

EXAMPLE   Symmetry can also be applied to three-dimensional objects. However, instead of being symmetrical around a line, three-dimensional objects are symmetrical around a plane. For example, a cube has many planes of symmetry:

A plane that passes through the midpoints of the vertical line segments creates two halves that are equal and have corresponding points on either side of the plane of symmetry.

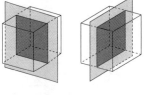

A plane can also pass through the midpoints of the horizontal line segments, either through the object's width or length. Each of these planes also creates two halves that are equal and have corresponding points on either side of the plane.

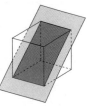

There are also planes that create symmetry by passing through the corners:

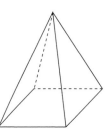

Directions   Draw and explain any planes of symmetry in the following three-dimensional objects.

1.

2.
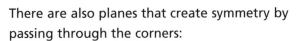

3.

4.
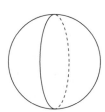

5.

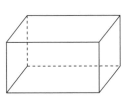

Geometry

Proportions

Find the missing value in the following proportion.

$$\frac{10}{15} = \frac{20}{x}$$

The outside elements, the 10 and the x, are called the *extremes*. The inside elements, the 15 and the 20, are called the *means*.

The theorem states that the product of the extremes = the product of the means. Write the following equation.

$10x = 300$ Divide both sides by 10 to get $x = 30$.

Directions Find the missing value in each proportion.

1. $\frac{3}{4} = \frac{x}{12}$ _____

2. $\frac{5}{8} = \frac{10}{x}$ _____

3. $\frac{11}{23} = \frac{44}{x}$ _____

4. $\frac{x}{3} = \frac{3}{9}$ _____

5. $\frac{7}{x} = \frac{12}{24}$ _____

6. $\frac{5}{x} = \frac{20}{24}$ _____

7. $\frac{2}{5} = \frac{8}{x}$ _____

8. $\frac{8}{13} = \frac{24}{x}$ _____

9. $\frac{x}{34} = \frac{11}{33}$ _____

10. $\frac{5}{9} = \frac{x}{27}$ _____

11. $\frac{19}{x} = \frac{20}{25}$ _____

12. $\frac{33}{33} = \frac{x}{24}$ _____

13. $\frac{8}{15} = \frac{x}{30}$ _____

14. $\frac{x}{60} = \frac{10}{24}$ _____

15. $\frac{4}{x} = \frac{12}{26}$ _____

Geometry

Determining Equal Ratios

EXAMPLE Determine if the following ratios are equal to each other. Use the theorem that the product of the extremes equals the product of the means.

$\frac{5}{3}$ and $\frac{25}{9}$

The product of the extremes, 5 and 9, is 45.

The product of the means, 3 and 25, is 75.

Since the product of the means must equal the product of the extremes in order for two ratios to be equal, these two ratios are not equal.

Directions Are the following ratios equal? Write *Yes* or *No*. Use the theorem that the product of the extremes equals the product of the means.

1. $\frac{5}{8}$ and $\frac{7}{10}$ _____

2. $\frac{6}{10}$ and $\frac{12}{20}$ _____

3. $\frac{8}{3}$ and $\frac{24}{9}$ _____

4. $\frac{2}{5}$ and $\frac{10}{25}$ _____

5. $\frac{9}{4}$ and $\frac{17}{8}$ _____

6. $\frac{35}{40}$ and $\frac{7}{8}$ _____

7. $\frac{10}{1}$ and $\frac{30}{1}$ _____

8. $\frac{15}{16}$ and $\frac{17}{18}$ _____

9. $\frac{21}{24}$ and $\frac{14}{16}$ _____

10. $\frac{60}{66}$ and $\frac{10}{11}$ _____

11. $\frac{99}{100}$ and $\frac{9}{10}$ _____

12. $\frac{85}{50}$ and $\frac{17}{10}$ _____

13. $\frac{6}{3}$ and $\frac{7}{4}$ _____

14. $\frac{9}{16}$ and $\frac{27}{48}$ _____

15. $\frac{36}{60}$ and $\frac{6}{10}$ _____

Corresponding Angles and Sides

EXAMPLE Name the corresponding angles and sides of the similar triangles.

m∠BAC = ?   m∠EDC

m∠ABC = ?   m∠DEC

m∠ACB = ?   m∠DCE

$\frac{AB}{?} = \frac{BC}{?}$ DE, EC

$\frac{BC}{?} = \frac{AC}{?}$ EC, DC

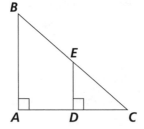

Directions Name the corresponding angles and sides of the similar triangles.

1. m∠P = ? _____

2. m∠Q = ? _____

3. m∠PRQ = ? _____

4. $\frac{QP}{?} = \frac{QR}{?}$ _____

5. $\frac{PR}{?} = \frac{QP}{?}$ _____

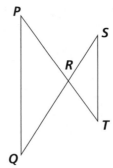

6. m∠A = ? _____

7. m∠B = ? _____

8. m∠C = ? _____

9. $\frac{AB}{?} = \frac{BC}{?}$ _____

10. $\frac{AC}{?} = \frac{AB}{?}$ _____

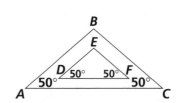

11. m∠A = ? _____

12. m∠B = ? _____

13. m∠C = ? _____

14. $\frac{AB}{?} = \frac{BC}{?}$ _____

15. $\frac{AC}{?} = \frac{AB}{?}$ _____

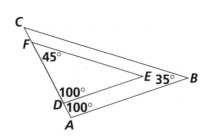

Using the AA Postulate

EXAMPLE Solve for the values of the unknowns
in this pair of similar triangles.

$x = ?$ 6

$y = ?$ 16

$z = ?$ 20

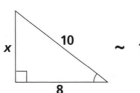 ~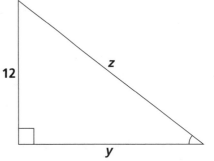

Directions Each pair of triangles is similar. Solve for the values of the unknowns.

1. $x = ?$ _____

2. $y = ?$ _____

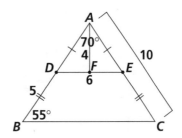

3. m∠BAD = ? _____

4. m∠DAC = ? _____

5. AC = ? _____

6. AD = ? _____

7. DC = ? _____

8. BD = ? _____

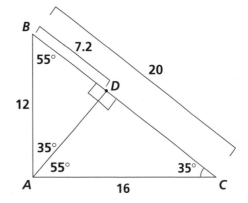

9. DF = ? _____

10. EF = ? _____

11. AD = ? _____

12. AE = ? _____

13. BC = ? _____

14. EC = ? _____

15. height of $\triangle ABC$ = ? _____

The Ratio of Similarity

EXAMPLE The ratio of similarity can be used to find the perimeters of similar nonregular polygons.

Given: The ratio of similarity between the two triangles is 1:3.

Find the perimeter of the larger polygon.

Use the ratio of similarity to find the measure of the larger triangle's sides: 9, 12, and 15. The sum of these is 36. Calculate the perimeter of the smaller triangle first, which is 12. If you use the ratio of similarity with the smaller triangle's perimeter, you get 36 as well.

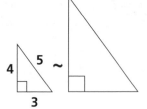

Directions Use the ratio of similarity to find the perimeter of the larger polygon.

1. The ratio of similarity is 1:4.

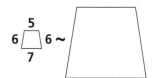

_____

2. The ratio of similarity is 3:4.

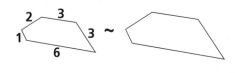

_____

3. The ratio of similarity is 2:3.

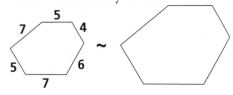

_____

4. The ratio of similarity is 3:5.

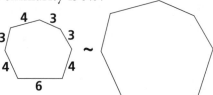

_____

5. The ratio of similarity is 5:8.

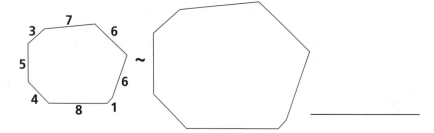

_____

Angle Measure in Regular Polygons

EXAMPLE The measure of an interior angle of a regular polygon = $180° - \frac{360°}{n}$
where n = number of sides.

regular octagon ($n = 8$)

angle measure = $180° - \frac{360°}{8} = 180° - 45° = 135°$

Directions Find the measure of each interior angle for a polygon with the given number of sides. Use the formula to calculate the measure.

1.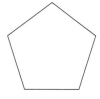

_____

2.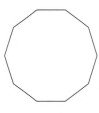

_____

3.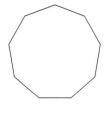

_____

4.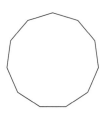

_____

5.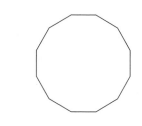

_____

Finding the Ratio of Similarity

EXAMPLE Find the ratio of similarity. It can be used to find the lengths of missing sides.

$\frac{\text{base of smaller triangle}}{\text{base of larger triangle}} = \frac{6}{12} = \frac{1}{2}$

hypotenuse of smaller triangle = 10

hyopotenuse of larger triangle = x

$\frac{1}{2} \cdot \frac{10}{x}$ $x = 20$

leg of smaller triangle = 8

leg of larger triangle = y

$\frac{8}{y} \cdot \frac{1}{2}$ $y = 16$

Directions Find the ratio of similarity in the following pairs of similar figures.

1. _____

2. 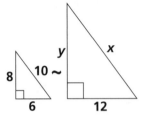 _____

3. 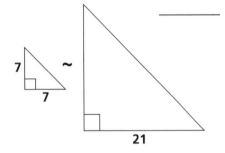 _____

4. _____

5.  _____

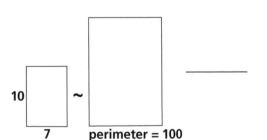
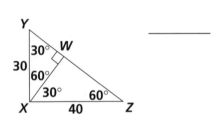
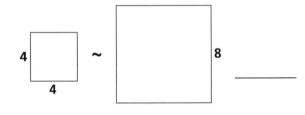

Dilating Images

EXAMPLE Give the coordinates of the image under the following dilation. Use graph paper to graph the object and its image. (All dilations have (0, 0) as the center of the dilation.)

Graph the image after dilating it by 3.

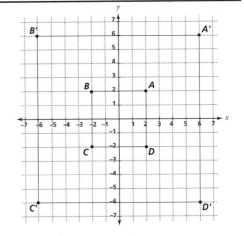

Directions Give the coordinates of the images under the following dilations. Use graph paper to graph each object and its images. (All dilations have (0, 0) as the center of the dilation.)

1. dilation of 2

2. dilation of 3

3. dilation of 4

4. dilation of 5

5. dilation of 6

6. dilation of 2

7. dilation of 3

8. dilation of 4

9. dilation of 5

10. dilation of 6

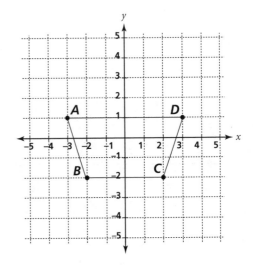

More Dilations

EXAMPLE	Give the coordinates of the image under the following dilation. Use graph paper to graph the object and its image. (All dilations have (0, 0) as the center of the dilation.)

Graph the image after dilating it by 2.

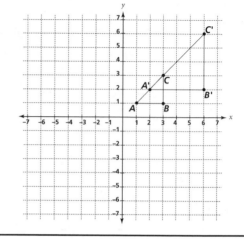

Directions Give the coordinates of the images under the following dilations.
Use graph paper to graph each object and its images.
(All dilations have (0, 0) as the center of the dilation.)

1. dilation of 2

2. dilation of 3

3. dilation of 4

4. dilation of 5

5. dilation of 6

6. dilation of 2

7. dilation of 3

8. dilation of 4

9. dilation of 5

10. dilation of 6

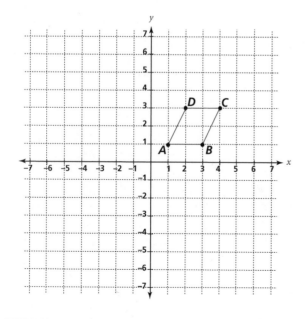

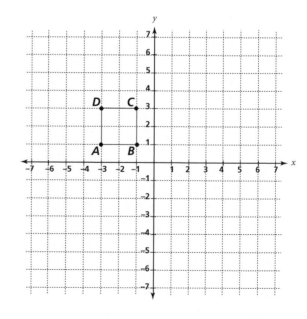

Shrinking Images

EXAMPLE | Give the coordinates of the image under the
following dilation. Use graph paper to graph
the object and its image. (All dilations have
(0, 0) as the center of the dilation.)

Graph the image after dilating it by $\frac{3}{5}$.

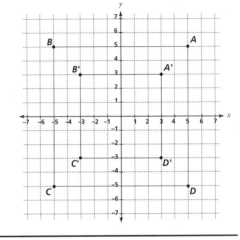

Directions Give the coordinates of the image under the following dilations.
Use graph paper to graph each object and its images.
(All dilations have (0, 0) as the center of the dilation.)

1. dilation of $\frac{1}{2}$

2. dilation of $\frac{1}{3}$

3. dilation of $\frac{1}{4}$

4. dilation of $\frac{1}{5}$

5. dilation of $\frac{1}{6}$

6. dilation of $\frac{5}{6}$

7. dilation of $\frac{2}{3}$

8. dilation of $\frac{1}{2}$

9. dilation of $\frac{1}{3}$

10. dilation of $\frac{1}{6}$

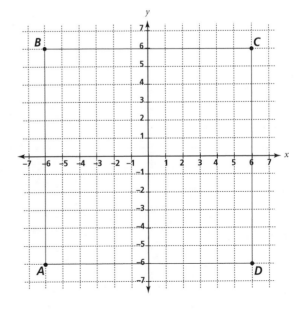

More Shrinking

EXAMPLE   Give the coordinates of the image under the following dilation. Use graph paper to graph the object and its image. (All dilations have (0, 0) as the center of the dilation.)

Graph the image after dilating it by $\frac{1}{5}$.

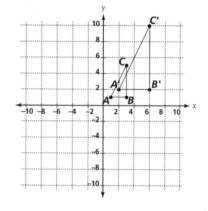

Directions   Give the coordinates of the image under the following dilations. Use graph paper to graph each object and its images. (All dilations have $(0, 0)$ as the center of the dilation.)

1. dilation of $\frac{1}{2}$

2. dilation of $\frac{2}{3}$

3. dilation of $\frac{3}{4}$

4. dilation of $\frac{4}{5}$

5. dilation of $\frac{5}{6}$

6. dilation of $\frac{1}{5}$

7. dilation of $\frac{2}{5}$

8. dilation of $\frac{3}{5}$

9. dilation of $\frac{4}{5}$

10. dilation of $\frac{1}{10}$

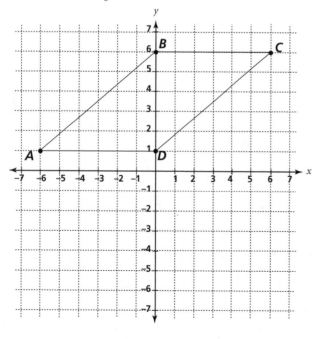

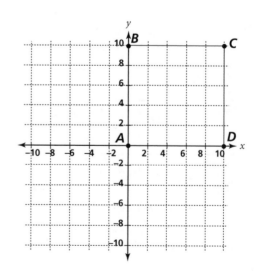

Zooming In

EXAMPLE   You can find differently scaled maps with the same center.

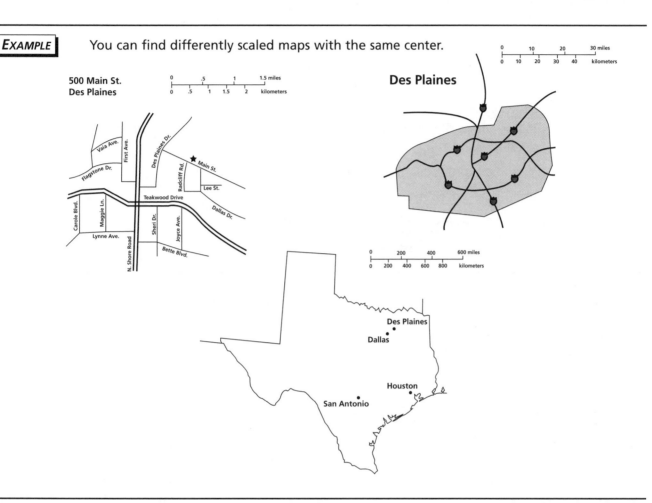

Directions   Use encyclopedias or atlases to choose a specific landmark or special landform. Then follow the directions to show each of the following.

1. Immediate field of vision—at landmark or landform

2. Town size

3. State size

4. Country size

5. World size

For example, if you choose Niagara Falls, you can map its location in Niagara and Niagara's location in the state of New York. Then you can map the state in relation to the country and then the world. Draw a sketched map of the places according to the given scale. Place a star on the center for the place that you chose.

Checking Triples

EXAMPLE   Check if the given set of numbers is a Pythagorean Triple. Use a calculator.

125, 300, 325

In order to check if a given set of numbers is a Pythagorean Triple, you must use the Pythagorean Theorem. If the sum of the squares of the two smaller numbers equals the square of the largest number, then the set of numbers is a Pythagorean Triple.

This can be expressed in the equation $a^2 + b^2 = c^2$.

You can now write the equation $125^2 + 300^2 = 325^2$.

This can be reduced to $15{,}625 + 90{,}000 = 105{,}625$.

Since this equation is true, the number set is a Pythagorean Triple.

Directions   Check if the given sets of numbers are Pythagorean Triples. Write *Yes* or *No*. Use a calculator.

1. (4, 5, 6) _____

2. (14, 15, 16) _____

3. (6, 8, 10) _____

4. (45, 79, 83) _____

5. (20, 399, 401) _____

6. (12, 35, 37) _____

7. (31, 225, 227) _____

8. (30, 72, 78) _____

9. (22, 27, 34) _____

10. (60, 80, 100) _____

11. (35, 84, 91) _____

12. (18, 25, 30) _____

13. (20, 47, 56) _____

14. (25, 60, 65) _____

15. (14, 21, 26) _____

Plato's Formula

EXAMPLE   Use Plato's Formula to find a Pythagorean Triple for the given integer.
Use a calculator. $m = 7$

Plato's Formula is $(2m)^2 + (m^2 - 1)^2 = (m^2 + 1)^2$

$$(2 \cdot 7)^2 + (7^2 - 1)^2 \stackrel{?}{=} (7^2 + 1)^2$$

$$14^2 + 48^2 \stackrel{?}{=} 50^2$$

The square root of both sides gives you a number set of 14, 48, and 50.

Check by squaring the numbers. If the equation is true, then the numbers
are a Pythagorean Triple. $96 + 2{,}304 = 2{,}500$
Since $196 + 2{,}304$ equals $2{,}500$, the numbers 14, 48, and 50 are a
Pythagorean Triple.

Directions   Use Plato's Formula to find Pythagorean Triples for the
given integers. Use a calculator.

1. $m = 4$ _____

2. $m = 5$ _____

3. $m = 8$ _____

4. $m = 9$ _____

5. $m = 11$ _____

6. $m = 12$ _____

7. $m = 13$ _____

8. $m = 14$ _____

9. $m = 16$ _____

10. $m = 17$ _____

11. $m = 18$ _____

12. $m = 19$ _____

13. $m = 21$ _____

14. $m = 22$ _____

15. $m = 30$ _____

Pythagorean Triples and Proofs

EXAMPLE Use the figure to find the following quantities:

Area of the large square = ?   26 • 26 = 676

Area of each triangle = ? $\frac{1}{2}(10 • 24) = \frac{1}{2}(240) = 120$

Area of the small square = ?   14 • 14 = 196

Sum of the areas that make up the large square = ?
120 + 120 + 120 + 120 + 196 = 676

Does the area of the large square equal the sum
of the areas of the four triangles plus the area
of the small square?   Yes

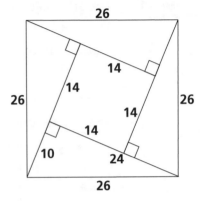

Directions Use the figures to find the following quantities.

1. Area of the large square = ? _____

2. Area of each triangle = ? _____

3. Area of the small square = ? _____

4. Sum of the areas that make up the large square = ?

_____

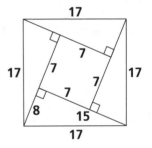

5. Does the area of the large square equal the sum of the areas
of the four triangles plus the area of the small square? _____

6. Area of the large square = ? _____

7. Area of each triangle = ? _____

8. Area of the small square = ? _____

9. Sum of the areas that make up the large square = ?

_____

10. Does the area of the large square equal the sum of the
areas of the four triangles plus the area of the small
square? _____

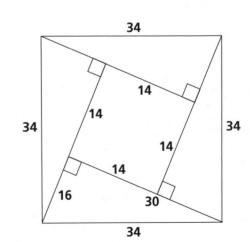

Pythagorean Demonstration

EXAMPLE

What is the area of each right triangle in Square I? 96

What is the length of each side of the inner square in Square I? 20

What is the area of the inner square in Square I? 400

What is the total area of Square I? 784

What is the sum of the areas of the four right triangles plus the area of the inner square?

$$96 + 96 + 96 + 96 + 400 = 784$$

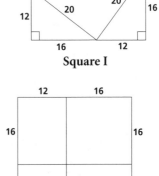

Square I

What is the area of the smaller square in Square II? 144

What is the area of the larger inside square in Square II? 256

What is the area of each rectangle in Square II? 192

What is the sum of the areas of the squares plus the areas of the rectangles?   144 + 256 + 192 + 192 = 784

How does the area of Square I compare to the area of Square II?   They are equal.

Directions   Use the figures to answer the questions.

1. What is the area of each right triangle in Square I? _____

2. What is the length of each side of the inner square in Square I? _____

3. What is the area of the inner square in Square I? _____

4. What is the total area of Square I? _____

5. What is the sum of the areas of the four right triangles plus the area of the inner square? _____

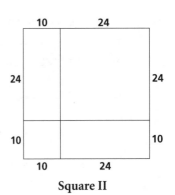

Square I

6. What is the area of the smaller square in Square II? _____

7. What is the area of the larger inside square in Square II? _____

8. What is the area of each rectangle in Square II? _____

9. What is the sum of the areas of the squares plus the areas of the rectangles? _____

10. How does the area of Square I compare to the area of Square II?

_____

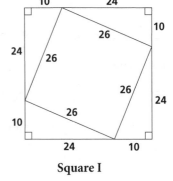

Square II

Pythagorean Theorem and Similar Triangles

EXAMPLE   △ABC is similar to both △DBA and △DAC.

△DBA is similar to △DAC.

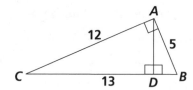

Directions   Use the figure to answer the following questions.

1. What is the length of $\overline{WZ}$?   _____

2. What is the length of $\overline{XZ}$?   _____

3. What is the length of $\overline{YZ}$?   _____

4. What segment makes up the hypotenuse of the largest triangle?   _____

5. What segment makes up the hypotenuse of the middle-sized triangle? _____

6. What segment makes up the hypotenuse of the smallest triangle?   _____

7. Is △WXZ similar to △WYZ? Why?   _____

8. What is the ratio of similarity between △WXY and △ZXW?   _____

9. What is the ratio of similarity between △WXY and △ZWY?   _____

10. What is the ratio of similarity between △ZXW and △ZWY?   _____

11. What is the perimeter of △WXY?   _____

12. What is the perimeter of △ZWY?   _____

13. What is the perimeter of △ZXW?   _____

14. What is the ratio between the three triangles' perimeters?   _____

15. Is the ratio between the three triangles' perimeters and the sides of the largest triangle the same?
    Hint: Divide each number of the perimeter ratio by each corresponding number in the largest triangle's side ratio. The results should be equal.

    _____

More with Similar Triangles

EXAMPLE   △ABC is similar to both △DAB and △DAC.

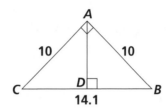

Directions   Use the figure to answer the following questions.

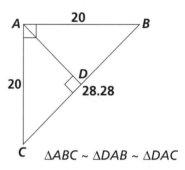

1. What is the length of $\overline{AD}$?   _____

2. What is the length of $\overline{BD}$?   _____

3. What is the length of $\overline{CD}$?   _____

4. What segment makes up the hypotenuse of the largest triangle?

_____

5. What segment makes up the hypotenuse of the left smaller triangle?   _____

6. What segment makes up the hypotenuse of the right smaller triangle?   _____

7. Is △DAB similar to △DAC? Why? _____

8. What is the ratio of similarity between △ABC and △DAB?   _____

9. What is the ratio of similarity between △ABC and △DAC?   _____

10. What is the ratio of similarity between △DAB and △DAC?   _____

11. What is the perimeter of △ABC?   _____

12. What is the perimeter of △DAB?   _____

13. What is the perimeter of △DAC?   _____

14. What is the ratio between the three triangles' perimeters?   _____

15. Is the ratio between the three triangles' perimeters and the sides of the largest triangle the same? **Hint:** Divide each number of the perimeter ratio by each corresponding number in the largest triangle's side ratio. The results should be equal.

_____

Pythagorean Proof and Trapezoids

EXAMPLE   Calculate the area of the trapezoid.

The formula to find the area of a trapezoid:

$$\text{area} = \frac{h(a + b)}{2}$$

$$\text{area} = \frac{5(14 + 16)}{2}$$

This can be simplified to area = $\frac{5(30)}{2}$ = 5 • 15 = 75.

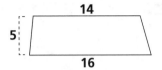

Directions   Calculate the area of each trapezoid.

1.

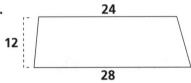

_____

2.

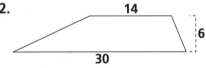

_____

3.

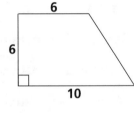

_____

4.

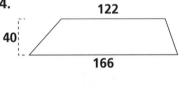

_____

5.

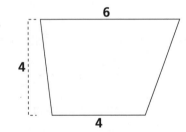

_____

6.

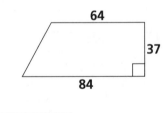

_____

7.

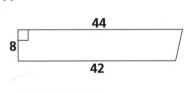

_____

8.

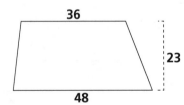

_____

9.

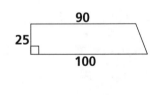

_____

10.

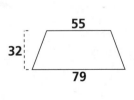

_____

Distance Formula

EXAMPLE   Complete the right triangle to find the distance between the two points. You may leave the distance in square root form.

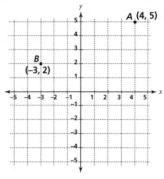

Calculate the distance. Distance $\overline{AB}$ is now the hypotenuse of a right triangle. You can then use the Pythagorean Theorem to calculate the distance by writing the equation $\overline{AB}^2 = 7^2 + 3^2$. This can be simplified to $\overline{AB}^2 = 49 + 9 = 58$. Take the square root of both sides to get $\overline{AB} = \sqrt{58}$.

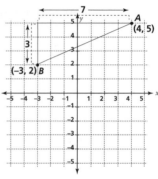

Directions   Complete the right triangle to find the distance between the named points. You may leave the distance in square root form.

1. A and B _____

2. A and C _____

3. A and D _____

4. A and E _____

5. B and C _____

6. B and D _____

7. B and E _____

8. C and D _____

9. C and E _____

10. D and E _____

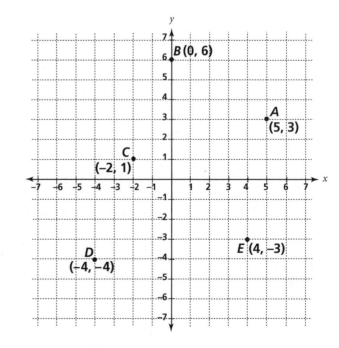

More Distance Formula

EXAMPLE   Use the distance formula to find the distances between the given points.

Given: $A = (0, 8)$ and $B = (-3, 4)$

Distance formula: $d = \sqrt{(x_2 - x_1)^2 + (y_2 - y_1)^2}$

You can write the equation $d = \sqrt{(-3 - 0)^2 + (4 - 8)^2}$.

This can be simplified to $d = \sqrt{(-3)^2 + (-4)^2} = \sqrt{9 + 16} = \sqrt{25} = 5$.

The distance between A and B is 5.

Directions   Use the distance formula to find the distances between the given points. You may leave your distance in square root form.

1. $(3, 2)$ and $(5, 7)$ _____

2. $(-3, 5)$ and $(4, -1)$ _____

3. $(0, 2)$ and $(-1, 4)$ _____

4. $(8, -5)$ and $(3, 6)$ _____

5. $(-6, -3)$ and $(-4, 2)$ _____

6. $(-4, 1)$ and $(5, 5)$ _____

7. $(0, 0)$ and $(7, 7)$ _____

8. $(-4, -5)$ and $(-6, -7)$ _____

9. $(9, 3)$ and $(3, -4)$ _____

10. $(7, 2)$ and $(3, -5)$ _____

11. $(3, -9)$ and $(-12, 4)$ _____

12. $(8, 2)$ and $(-1, 0)$ _____

13. $(8, 8)$ and $(0, 7)$ _____

14. $(2, 3)$ and $(-4, -3)$ _____

15. $(-8, 11)$ and $(-4, 5)$ _____

Converse of the Pythagorean Theorem

EXAMPLE The converse of the Pythagorean Theorem states that for a triangle to be a
right triangle, its sides must conform to the equation $a^2 + b^2 = c^2$. Test this
triple: 14, 48, 50

$$14^2 + 48^2 = 50^2$$

If the equation is true, then the triple could be the sides of a right triangle.
If we simplify the above statement, we get $196 + 2304 = 2500$. Since this is a
true statement, the triple can be the sides of a right triangle.

Directions Use the converse of the Pythagorean Theorem to test whether or not these
triples can be the sides of a right triangle. Answer *Yes* or *No*.

1. 50, 624, 626 _____

2. 80, 1599, 1601 _____

3. 3, 6, 8 _____

4. 7, 37, 39 _____

5. 12, 37, 39 _____

6. 21, 109, 111 _____

7. 17, 71.25, 73.25 _____

8. 16, 65, 67 _____

9. 31, 255, 257 _____

10. 24, 143, 145 _____

11. 36, 323, 325 _____

12. 48, 2303, 2305 _____

13. 1, 1, 2 _____

14. 50, 625, 627 _____

15. 60, 899, 901 _____

Architecture and Geometric Shapes

EXAMPLE   Triangles are used in buildings for support and
design. Builders may use the Pythagorean Theorem
to calculate the length of a side of a right triangle.
If a triangle is a right triangle with legs *a* and *b*
and hypotenuse *c*, then $a^2 + b^2 + = c^2$.

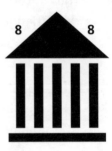

$$8^2 + 8^2 = c^2 \qquad 64 + 64 = c^2$$
$$128 = c^2 \qquad c = \sqrt{128} \qquad c = 11.31$$

Directions   Use the Pythagorean Theorem to solve for *x*. Use a calculator and round
to the nearest hundredth.

1.

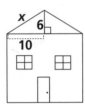

_____

2.

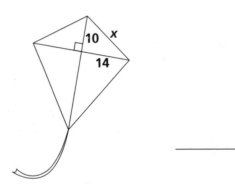

_____

3.

_____

4.

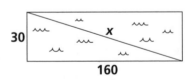

_____

5.

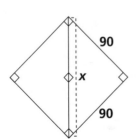

_____

Perimeters of Polygons

EXAMPLE   Find the perimeter of the figure.

The perimeter of a polygon is the sum of the lengths
of all the sides of the polygon.

Write the equation.

perimeter = 24 + 13 + 18 + 34 + 41 + 12 + 16 + 24 + 13 + 28

This can be simplified to perimeter = 223.

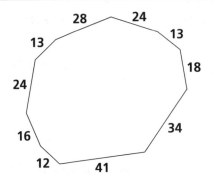

Directions   Find the perimeter of each figure.

1.
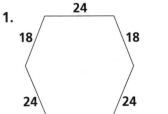
_____

2.
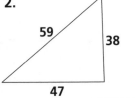
_____

3.
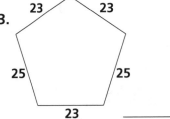
_____

4.
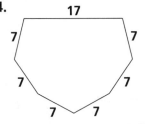
_____

5.
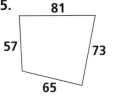
_____

6.
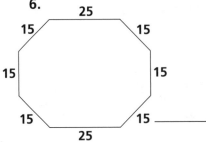
_____

7.

_____

8.
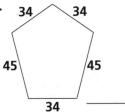
_____

9.
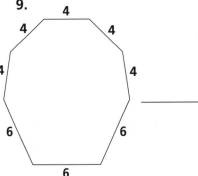
_____

10.
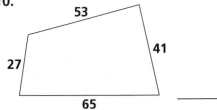
_____

Perimeter Formulas

EXAMPLE   The formula to calculate the perimeter of a rectangle is $P = 2(b + h)$.

You are given a value of 65 for b and a value of 87 for h.

You can write the equation $P = 2(65 + 87)$.

This can be simplified to $P = 2(152) = 304$.

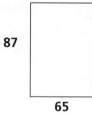
87

65

Directions   Use formulas to calculate the rectangle or parallelogram perimeters.

1.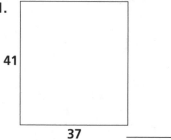

41

37

_____

2.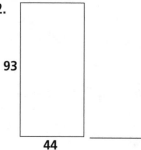

93

44

_____

3.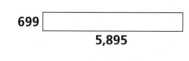

18

76

_____

4.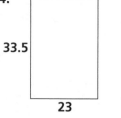

33.5

23

_____

5.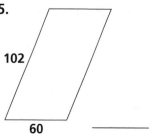

102

60

_____

6.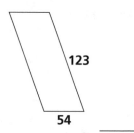

123

54

_____

7.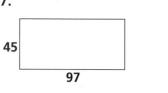

45

97

_____

8.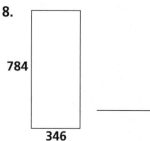

784

346

_____

9.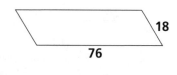

699

5,895

_____

10.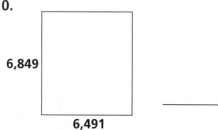

6,849

6,491

_____

Perimeters and Diagonals

EXAMPLE Use the Pythagorean Theorem to find the perimeter of △ABC.

Calculate the length of $\overline{AC}$. The length of 12 for the base $\overline{DC}$ and 5 for the height $\overline{AD}$ are given. Write the equation:
$\overline{AC}^2 = 12^2 + 5^2$. This can be simplified to $\overline{AC}^2 = 144 + 25 = 169$.

Take the square root of both sides to get $\overline{AC} = 13$.

You know that the parallel sides of a rectangle are equal. Therefore, you know that side $\overline{AB}$ is the same length as base $\overline{DC}$, which is 12.
You also know that side $\overline{BC}$ is the same length as height $\overline{AD}$, which is 5.

You can now write an equation for the perimeter of △ABC, $P = 13 + 12 + 5 = 30$.

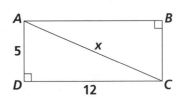

Directions Use the Pythagorean Theorem to find the missing side. Then calculate the perimeter. Use a calculator and round to the nearest tenth.

1.

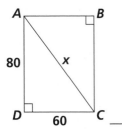

_____

2.

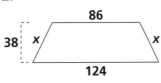

_____

3.

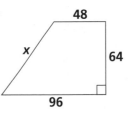

_____

4.

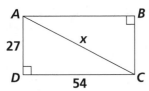

_____

5.

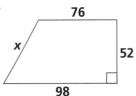

_____

6.

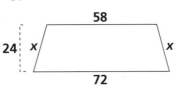

_____

7.

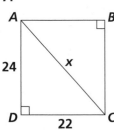

_____

8.

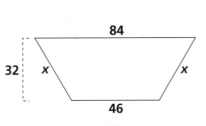

_____

9.

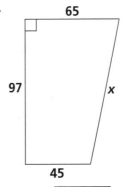

_____

10.

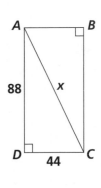

_____

Parallelogram Areas

EXAMPLE   Find the area of the parallelogram.

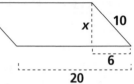

Use the Pythagorean Theorem to find the length of x, which is the height of the parallelogram. The length of 10 for the hypotenuse of the triangle and a length of 6 for the base are given.

Write the equation $10^2 = 6^2 + x^2$. This can be simplified to $100 = 36 + x^2$. Subtract 36 from both sides to get $x^2 = 64$. Take the square root of both sides to get $x = 8$. Now that you have a value of 8 for the height of the parallelogram, you can write an equation for its area.

$$\text{area} = 20 \bullet 8 = 160$$

Directions   Find the area of each parallelogram.

1.

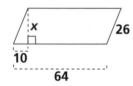

_____

2.

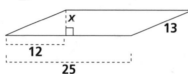

_____

3.

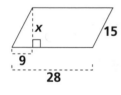

_____

4.

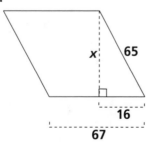

_____

5.

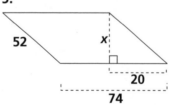

_____

6.

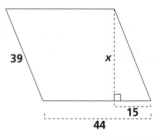

_____

7.

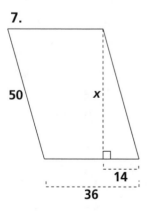

_____

8.

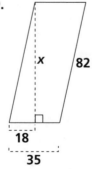

_____

9.

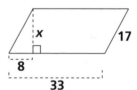

_____

10.

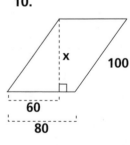

_____

Areas of Trapezoids

EXAMPLE   Use what you know about the area of a trapezoid to find the values
of the average base. The formula for the area of a trapezoid is
area = (average base) • (height).

You are given a value of 300 for the area and 10 for the height.

10 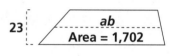 Area = 300

You can write the equation 300 = average base • 10.
Divide both sides by 10 to get average base = 30.

Directions   Use what you know about the area of a trapezoid to find the values
of the following unknowns.

1.

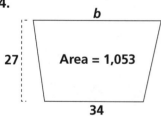

19   ab
     Area = 456

2.

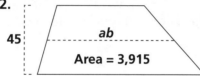

45   ab
     Area = 3,915

3.

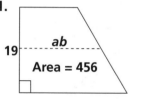

23   ab
     Area = 1,702

4.

b
27   Area = 1,053
34

5.

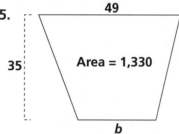

49
35   Area = 1,330
b

6.

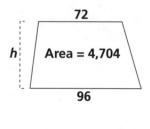

72
h   Area = 4,704
96

7.

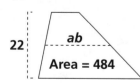

22   ab
     Area = 484

8.

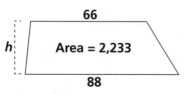

66
h   Area = 2,233
88

9.

b
47   Area = 3,243
42

10.

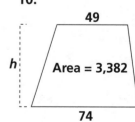

49
h   Area = 3,382
74

Geometry

Heron's Formula

EXAMPLE Use Heron's Formula to find the area of a triangle with given side lengths. Use a calculator and round to the nearest tenth.

Heron's Formula states that the area of a triangle = $\sqrt{s(s-a)(s-b)(s-c)}$ where $s = \frac{1}{2}(a+b+c)$.

First calculate s. You can write the equation $s = \frac{1}{2}(15 + 19 + 23)$. This can be simplified to $s = \frac{1}{2}(57) = 28.5$.

Now you can write the equation: area = 28.5(28.5 − 15)(28.5 − 19)(28.5 − 23).

This can be simplified to area = $\sqrt{28.5(13.5)(9.5)(5.5)}$ = $\sqrt{20,103.2}$ = 141.8.

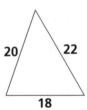

Directions Use Heron's Formula to find the area of each triangle with the given side lengths. Use a calculator and round to the nearest tenth.

1. 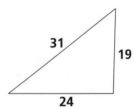 _____

2. 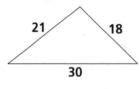 _____

3. 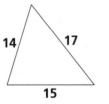 _____

4. 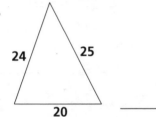 _____

5. 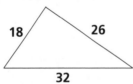 _____

6. _____

7. 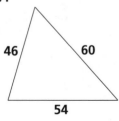 _____

8. 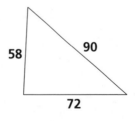 _____

9. 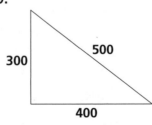 _____

10. 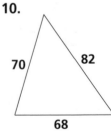 _____

Tessellations

EXAMPLE   M.C. Ecsher was an artist who used geometric figures to create drawings. He became famous for his intricate designs created by repetitive patterns. Study the tessellation to see some of the varied patterns that can be created with simple geometric shapes.

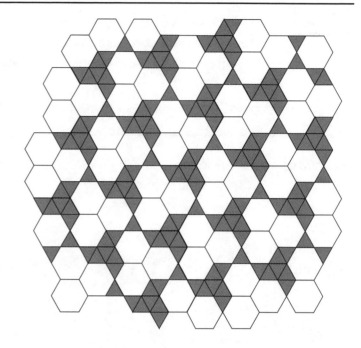

Directions   Try the following.

1. Make a tessellation using three different shapes of varying sizes.

2. Make a tessellation using an irregular polygon.

3. Make a tessellation using a shape that has curves in it.

4. Make a tessellation by mixing regular and irregular polygons.

5. Find three objects that have tessellations in their design.

Definition of a Circle

| EXAMPLE | The radius of a circle is the distance between the center and any point on the circle. The diameter of a circle is twice as long as the radius of the same circle. The circumference is $2\pi r$ where r is the radius of the circle.

What is the diameter of the circle with center *X*?   24 units

Directions Use the information about radius, diameter, and circumference to answer the following questions.

1. What is the diameter of the circle with center *A*?

_____

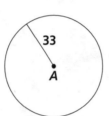

2. What is the diameter of the circle with center *B*?

_____

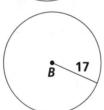

3. What is the radius of the circle with center *C*?

_____

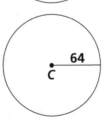

4. What is the circumference of the circle with center *D*?

_____

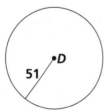

5. What is the diameter of the circle with center *E*?

_____

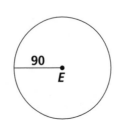

6. What is the circumference of the circle with center *F*?

_____

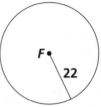

7. What is the radius of the circle with center *G*?

_____

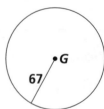

8. What is the diameter of the circle with center *H*?

_____

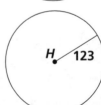

9. What is the circumference of the circle with center *I*?

_____

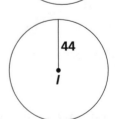

10. What is the diameter of the circle with center *J*?

_____

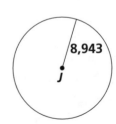

The Ratio π

EXAMPLE   Find the diameter and the radius of a circle with the given circumference.

$C = 66\pi$ in.

The formula for the circumference of a circle is

$C = 2\pi r$, where r equals the radius and C equals the circumference.

$r = \frac{C}{2\pi}$

$r = \frac{66\pi}{2\pi}$

$r = 33$ in.

The diameter of a circle equals two times the radius or $2r$.

Therefore, the diameter of this circle is 66 in.

Directions   Find the diameter and the radius of a circle with the given circumference.

1. $C = 25\pi$ ft   _____ _____

2. $C = 46\pi$ in.   _____ _____

3. $C = 18\pi$ cm   _____ _____

4. $C = 87\pi$ m   _____ _____

5. $C = 65\pi$ mm   _____ _____

6. $C = 28\pi$ ft   _____ _____

7. $C = 78\pi$ in.   _____ _____

8. $C = 32\pi$ cm   _____ _____

9. $C = 20\pi$ m   _____ _____

10. $C = 824\pi$ mm   _____ _____

11. $C = 608\pi$ ft   _____ _____

12. $C = 754\pi$ in.   _____ _____

13. $C = 589\pi$ cm   _____ _____

14. $C = 1,098\pi$ m   _____ _____

15. $C = 5,318\pi$ mm   _____ _____

Approximating the Area of a Circle

EXAMPLE Use the estimation formula to calculate the area of a circle
with the following diameter or radius.

$r = 3$ units

The estimation formula for the area of a circle is area $\approx 3r^2$.

Write an equation to estimate the area using the above radius.

area $\approx 3(3)^2$.

This can be simplified to area $\approx 3(9) = 27$ sq units.

Directions Use the estimation formula to calculate the area of a circle
with the following diameter or radius.

1. $d = 12$ _____

2. $r = 12$ _____

3. $d = 24$ _____

4. $r = 13$ _____

5. $d = 40$ _____

6. $d = 60$ _____

7. $r = 8$ _____

8. $r = 19$ _____

9. $d = 64$ _____

10. $r = 25$ _____

Directions Estimate the radius of the circle for the given areas.

11. $A \approx 75$ _____

12. $A \approx 147$ _____

13. $A \approx 243$ _____

14. $A \approx 363$ _____

15. $A \approx 507$ _____

Area and Probability

$$\text{Probability} = \frac{\text{Area of Desired Outcome}}{\text{Total Area}}$$

Find the probability of a point being in the shaded area.
If you were to draw two segments that connected the
opposite midpoints of the rectangle's segments, you would
see that the shaded areas of each quarter of the rectangle
equal the unshaded areas of each quarter of the rectangle.

Since the amount of shaded area equals the amount of
unshaded area, the probability of a point being in the
shaded area is 50%.

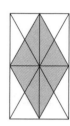

Directions   Find the probability of a point being in the shaded area.

1.

_____

2.

_____

3.

_____

4.

_____

5.

_____

Formula for the Area of a Circle

EXAMPLE   Find the radius of a circle with the given area. Use a calculator and round
the answer to the nearest tenth.

$$A = 900 \text{ cm}^2$$

The formula for the area of a circle is $A = \pi r^2$.

You can find the radius by substituting the given area of 900 cm² for A in
the equation.

$$900 \text{ cm}^2 = \pi r^2$$

$$\frac{900}{\pi} = r^2$$

$$\sqrt{\frac{900}{\pi}} = r$$

$$16.9 \text{ cm} = r$$

Directions   Find the radius of a circle with the given area. Use a calculator and round the
answer to the nearest tenth.

1. $A = 400 \text{ cm}^2$ _____

2. $A = 876 \text{ cm}^2$ _____

3. $A = 93 \text{ cm}^2$ _____

4. $A = 542 \text{ cm}^2$ _____

5. $A = 650 \text{ cm}^2$ _____

6. $A = 764 \text{ cm}^2$ _____

7. $A = 410 \text{ cm}^2$ _____

8. $A = 999 \text{ cm}^2$ _____

9. $A = 10,000 \text{ cm}^2$ _____

10. $A = 2,340 \text{ cm}^2$ _____

More Formula for the Area of a Circle

EXAMPLE   Use the formula to find the area. Use a calculator and round the answer to
the nearest tenth.

radius = 5.2 in.	diameter = 7 ft
$A = \pi r^2$	$A = \frac{1}{4}\pi d^2$
$A = \pi(5.2)^2$	$A = (\frac{1}{4})\pi(7)^2$
$A = \pi(27.04)$	$A = (\frac{1}{4})\pi(49)$
$A = 84.9$ sq in.	$A = 38.5$ sq ft

Directions   Find the area of a circle with the given radius or diameter. Use a calculator and round
the answer to the nearest tenth.

1. $r = 6.4$ in.   _____

2. $r = 9.4$ ft   _____

3. $d = 6.2$ cm   _____

4. $r = 7.4$ units   _____

5. $d = 16$ ft   _____

6. $d = 17$ in.   _____

7. $r = 6.5$ cm   _____

8. $r = 10$ in.   _____

9. $d = 63$ mm   _____

10. $d = 30$ units   _____

Circles and Their Angles and Sectors

EXAMPLE Find the value of the inscribed angle.

By the theorem, an inscribed angle measures
one half of its intercepted arc.

The intercepted arc measures 90°.

Therefore, the inscribed angle measures $\frac{90}{2} = 45°$.

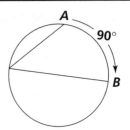

Directions Find the value of the unknown.

1. inscribed angle

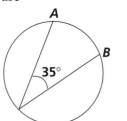

_____

2. arc

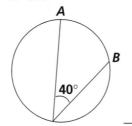

_____

3. inscribed angle

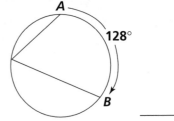

_____

4. arc

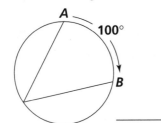

_____

5. inscribed angle

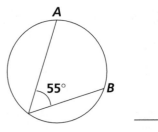

_____

6. arc

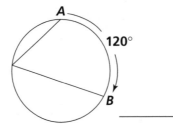

_____

7. inscribed angle

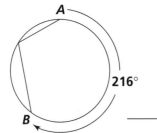

_____

8. arc

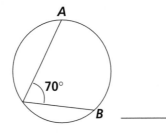

_____

9. inscribed angle

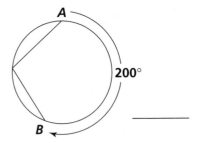

_____

10. arc

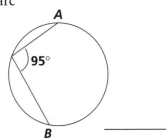

_____

Tangents, Circumcircles, and Incircles

EXAMPLE

What is the largest circle you can fit into △ABC?

The incircle is the largest circle that will fit into △ABC.

To construct the incircle, construct the angle bisectors for two of the triangle's three angles. The point where the bisectors meet will be the center of the incircle. Label this point X.

To find the exact distance of the circle's radius, construct a line that is perpendicular to any side of the triangle that passes through X. Label the point where this perpendicular meets the triangle's side Y. $\overline{XY}$ is the length of the incircle's radius.

Draw the incircle using X as the center and length $\overline{XY}$ as the radius.

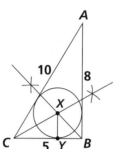

Directions Complete the following constructions on a separate sheet of paper.

1. Construct the incircle for △DEF.

2. Construct the circumcircle for △DEF.

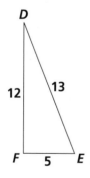

3. Construct the incircle for △XYZ.

4. Construct the circumcircle for △XYZ.

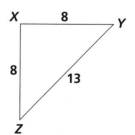

5. Construct the incircle and the circumcircle for △PQR.

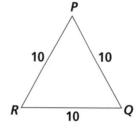

Sine, Cosine, and Tangent

EXAMPLE Find the sine, cosine, and tangent for angle *x*.

sine *x* = $\frac{\text{opposite}}{\text{hypotenuse}}$ sine *x* = $\frac{3}{5}$ = 0.6

cosine *x* = $\frac{\text{adjacent}}{\text{hypotenuse}}$ cosine *x* = $\frac{4}{5}$ = 0.8

tangent *x* = $\frac{\text{opposite}}{\text{adjacent}}$ tangent *x* = $\frac{3}{4}$ = 0.75

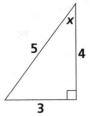

Directions Find the sine, cosine, and tangent for angle *x*.

1.

sine _____

cosine _____

tangent _____

4.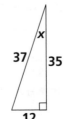

sine _____

cosine _____

tangent _____

2.

sine _____

cosine _____

tangent _____

5.

sine _____

cosine _____

tangent _____

3.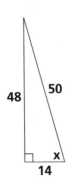

sine _____

cosine _____

tangent _____

Spheres

EXAMPLE   Find the surface area and the volume for a sphere with the given diameter.
Use a calculator and round your answer to the nearest hundredth.

   $d = 4$

The formula for the surface area of a sphere is $4\pi r^2$. You know that $r =$
the radius and is $\frac{1}{2}$ of the diameter, d. The radius for this sphere is 2.

You can write the equation surface area = $4\pi(2^2)$. This can be reduced
to surface area = $4\pi4 = 16\pi$.

Using your calculator, you can multiply 16 times π to get 50.26.

The formula for the volume of a sphere is volume = $\frac{4}{3}\pi r^3$.

You can write the equation volume = $\frac{4}{3}\pi(2^3)$. This can be reduced
to volume = $\frac{4}{3}\pi8 = 6\pi = 18.85$.

Directions   Find the surface area and the volume of spheres with the given diameters.
Use a calculator and round your answer to the nearest hundredth.

1. $d = 10$ units $S =$ _____ $V =$ _____

2. $d = 6$ units $S =$ _____ $V =$ _____

3. $d = 8$ units $S =$ _____ $V =$ _____

4. $d = 2$ units $S =$ _____ $V =$ _____

5. $d = 14$ units $S =$ _____ $V =$ _____

6. $d = 16$ units $S =$ _____ $V =$ _____

7. $d = 18$ units $S =$ _____ $V =$ _____

8. $d = 20$ units $S =$ _____ $V =$ _____

9. $d = 50$ units $S =$ _____ $V =$ _____

10. $d = 100$ units $S =$ _____ $V =$ _____

Pie Charts

EXAMPLE   Graph a pie chart of the following data. A die was rolled 30 times. The number of times that each number from 1–6 was rolled was as follows:

#1 7 times   **#2** 4 times   **#3** 5 times   **#4** 6 times   **#5** 3 times   **#6** 5 times

Figure out the percentage of the total number of rolls for each number. Divide the number of rolls for each number by the total number of rolls. Then multiply that number by 100. For example, the number 4 was rolled 6 times out of 30. $\frac{6}{30} = 0.2$. $0.2 \cdot 100 = 20\%$. Do this for each number.

#1 $0.2333 = 23.33\%$ **#2** $0.1333 = 13.33\%$ **#3** $0.1666 = 16.66\%$

#4 $0.2 = 20\%$ **#5** $0.1 = 10\%$ **#6** $0.1666 = 16.66\%$

Check by adding the percentages to get the total equal to 100% (or about that amount with rounding). Then figure out how big a sector of a circle each of the percentages is. Divide the percentages by 100 to get the decimals. Multiply the number of degrees in a circle, 360, by the decimal to find the size, in degrees, of a sector. Divide the circle to make the pie chart.

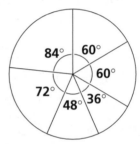

Directions   On a separate sheet of paper, make a pie chart illustrating each of the following sets of data.

1. The number of boys vs. the number of girls in your class.

2. The number of people in your class who were born in each month of the year.

3. The number of people in your class with the following eye colors: blue, brown, green, or gray.

4. The number of right-handed vs. left-handed people in your class.

5. The number of people in your class wearing glasses, contacts, or no corrective lenses.

Basic Volume Formulas

EXAMPLE   The formula for the volume of a rectangular solid is
$V = l \cdot w \cdot h$. You are given a value of 24,000 for V,
and values of 20 and 40 for l and w.

Write the equation $24{,}000 = 20 \cdot 40 \cdot x$, to solve for x.
This can be reduced to $24{,}000 = 800 \cdot x$. Divide both
sides by 800 to get $x = 30$.

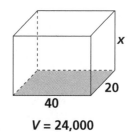

$V = 24{,}000$

Directions   Use what you know about volumes to find the unknown.

1.

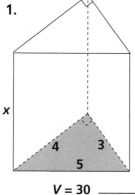

$V = 30$ _____

2.

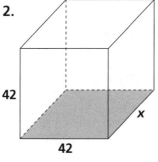

$V = 74{,}088$ _____

3.

$V = 1{,}200$ _____

4.

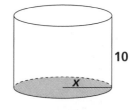

$V = 576$ _____

5.

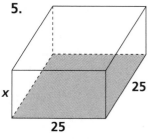

$V = 7{,}500$ _____

6.

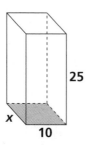

$V = 2{,}500$ _____

7.

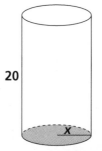

$V = 2{,}260.8$ _____

8.

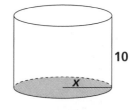

$V = 1{,}538.6$ _____

9.

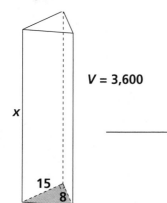

$V = 3{,}600$ _____

10.

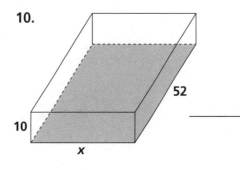

$V = 18{,}720$ _____

Volumes of Pyramids and Cones

EXAMPLE Find the volume of the following cone.

The formula for the volume of a cone or pyramid is
$V = \frac{1}{3}$(area of base)(height).

You are given a value of 3 for the radius of the base. Calculate the area of
the base using the formula for the area of a circle, area = πr^2.

Write an equation for the area of the base, area = $\pi 3^2$. This can be simplified to area = $\pi 9$ = 28.3.

Write an equation for the volume of the cone, $V = \frac{1}{3}$(28.3)(9) = 84.9.

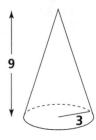

Directions Find the volume of each pyramid or cone.

1.

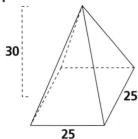

30

25

25

_____

2.

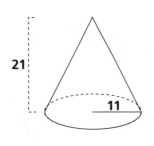

21

11

_____

3.

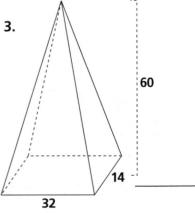

60

14

32

_____

4.

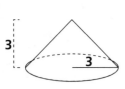

3

3

_____

5.

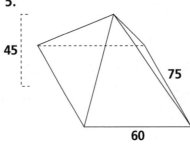

45

75

60

_____

Surface Areas of Prisms and Cylinders

EXAMPLE | The formula for the surface area of a rectangular prism is

$$SA = 2(lw + hl + hw).$$

You are given values of 5, 7, and 6 for *l*, *w,* and *h*.

Write the equation $SA = 2((5 \cdot 7)+(5 \cdot 6)+(6 \cdot 7))$. This can be reduced to $SA = 2(35 + 30 + 42) = 2(107) = 214.$

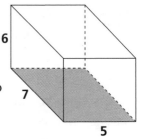

Directions Find the surface area of each of the following three-dimensional figures. Round your answer to the nearest hundredth.

1. 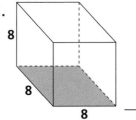 _____

2. 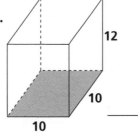 _____

3. 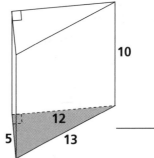 _____

4. 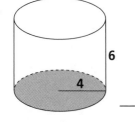 _____

5. 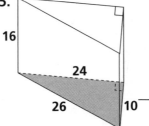 _____

6. 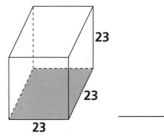 _____

7. 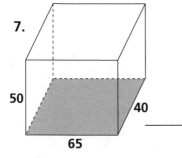 _____

8. 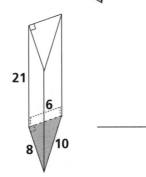 _____

9. 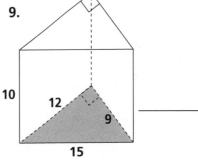 _____

10. 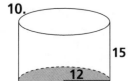 _____

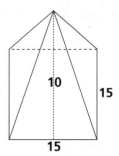
Surface Areas of Pyramids and Cones

EXAMPLE   Find the surface area of this pyramid. The formula for the surface area of a pyramid is SA = area of base + area of four triangles.

$$SA = (s \cdot s) + \tfrac{1}{2}sl + \tfrac{1}{2}sl + \tfrac{1}{2}sl + \tfrac{1}{2}sl = s^2 + 2sl \text{ where}$$
l is the measure of the slant height.

You are given a value of 15 for s and a value of 10 for l.

Write the equation $SA = 15^2 + 2(15 \cdot 10)$.
This can be simplified to $SA = 225 + 300 = 525$.

Directions   Find the surface area of these pyramids and cones. Round your answer to the nearest hundredth.

1.
13, 7, 13

_____

2.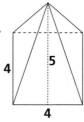
7, 4

_____

3.
4, 5, 4

_____

4.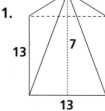
5, 6

_____

5.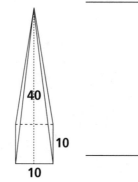
40, 10, 10

_____

6.
5, 9

_____

7.
13, 5, 13

_____

8.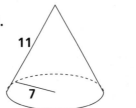
11, 7

_____

9.
18, 24, 18

_____

10.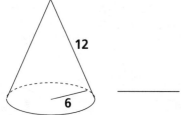
12, 6

_____

Measurements

Complete the following statement.

14 pints = ____ gallons

You know that 1 gallon equals 4 quarts. You also know that 1 quart equals
2 pints. Therefore, 1 gallon = 4 quarts = 8 pints.

If you substitute 8 pints for gallons, you can write the following equation.

14 pints = x(8 pints). Divide both sides by 8 pints to get x = 1.75 gallons.

Directions Complete each statement.

1. 5 ft = _____ in.

2. 13 yd = _____ ft

3. 56 in. = _____ ft

4. 7 mi = _____ yd

5. 58,080 ft = _____ mi

6. 78 gallons = _____ qt

7. 28 cups = _____ pints

8. 304 ounces = _____ lb

9. 15 cups = _____ fl oz

10. 90,000 lb = _____ tons

11. 66 kg = _____ g

12. 57 L = _____ mL

13. 92 cm = _____ mm

14. 843 cm = _____ m

15. 88 km = _____ cm

16. 85 ft = _____ in.

17. 36 yd = _____ ft

18. 1,008 in. = _____ ft

19. 12 mi = _____ yd

20. 290,400 ft = _____ mi

Unfolding Three-Dimensional Objects

EXAMPLE
Imagine that this cube is hollow. How could you unfold it so that its faces lie flat on a plane? You know that the figure is a cube. A cube has six identical square faces. But how would these six faces be arranged if laid flat?

Picture yourself holding a cube by pressing your index fingers to the middle of two opposite sides. Holding the cube like this, you could "roll" the cube on the ground between your fingers.

Each of the four faces that you are not touching would, in turn, touch the ground. Therefore, each of these four faces would lie next to each other in a line if you were to unfold the cube and lie it flat. But what about the two faces that you are holding? These will have to be attached to either side of the line so that they could be folded to cover the "sides" of the cube like this:

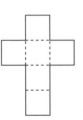

Directions   Unfold and draw the following three-dimensional figures. Use a separate sheet of paper.

1.

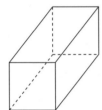

2.

3.

4.

5.

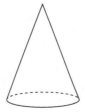

Lines and Planes in Space

EXAMPLE Review the following.

A line that does not intersect an object shares no points
in common with it.

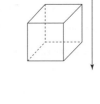

A line that is tangent to an object
touches it at only one point.

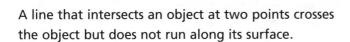

A line that intersects an object at two points crosses
the object but does not run along its surface.

A line that shares all of its points with an object runs
along the object's surface.

Directions Given a plane and a cube in space, draw a sketch of and then
describe the following. Use a separate sheet of paper.

1. The plane and the cube have one point in common.

2. The plane and the cube share a line of points in common.

3. The plane and the cube share the perimeter of a square in common.

4. The plane and the cube share the area of a square in common.

5. The plane and the cube share no points in common.

Loci in the Coordinate Plane

EXAMPLE   Find the loci of points 2 units from the origin. Draw a sketch and write the equation.

You know that the loci of points equidistant from one point form a circle with a radius that is equal to the distance given. Therefore, the loci of points 2 units from the origin will form a circle with the origin as the center and a radius of 2. You can draw this using a compass. It will look like this:

You know that the formula for a circle with radius r and center $(0, 0)$ is $r^2 = x^2 + y^2$. Therefore, the equation for this circle is $2^2 = x^2 + y^2$. This can be simplified to $4 = x^2 + y^2$.

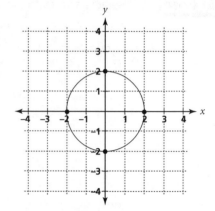

Directions   Find the loci. Draw a sketch on a separate sheet of paper. Then write the equation.

1. Loci of points 7 units from the origin   _____

2. Loci of points 8 units from the origin   _____

3. Loci of points 9 units from the origin   _____

4. Loci of points 10 units from the origin   _____

5. Loci of points 20 units from the origin   _____

Compound Loci

| EXAMPLE | Sketch, then describe, the following compound loci: The intersection of two planes and a sphere where each plane crosses the sphere to form a great circle. |

You know that the intersection of two planes forms a line. You also know that in order for a great circle to be formed by the intersection of a plane and a sphere, the plane must pass through the circle's center.

In order for both planes to cross each other and form great circles with the sphere, the line formed by the crossing planes must pass through the sphere's center.

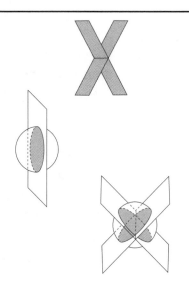

Directions   Sketch and describe the following compound loci.

1. The intersection of a triangular prism with a plane where the plane crosses through the side of one of the bases and a vertex of the other base

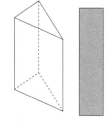

2. The intersection of a triangle-based pyramid and a plane that is parallel with the base of the pyramid

3. The intersection of an ellipse-based cone and a plane where the plane is parallel with the base

4. The intersection of a plane and a cone where the plane is perpendicular to the base and passes through the point of the cone

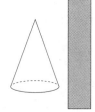

5. The intersection of a cone and a plane in which the plane is not parallel with the base but does intersect the base

---

The Fibonacci Series

EXAMPLE   Examine the following.

The equiangular spiral of a nautilus shell is a spiral that is based on a series of numbers called the Fibonacci series. The series is named after Leonardo Fibonacci (c. 1170–c. 1240) of Pisa, Italy, who rediscovered the sequence through his readings of classical Greek mathematicians. The sequence starts at 0 and continues 0, 1, 1, 2, 3, 5, 8, 13 . . . In order to find the next number, you add the last two numbers in the sequence.

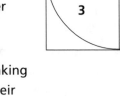

The Fibonacci spiral is a spiral that is drawn by making an array of squares with Fibonacci numbers for their sides. By drawing quarter circles through the squares, the spiral shape of a nautilus shell appears.

Directions   Do the following constructions on the coordinate plane.

1. A series of circles with the origin as the center, whose radii follow the Fibonacci series. Draw circles for the first 6 numbers in the sequence and draw them on the same coordinate plane graph.

2. A series of shapes that have the following endpoints and substitute the Fibonacci numbers for x: $(0, x)$, $(x, 0)$, $(0, -x)$, $(-x, 0)$

3. A series of shapes that have the following endpoints and substitute the Fibonacci numbers for x: $(0, 0)$, (x, x), $(-x, x)$.

4. A series of shapes that have the following endpoints and substitute the Fibonacci numbers for x: (x, x), $(2x, x)$, $(2x, -x)$, $(x, -x)$.

5. A series of shapes that have the following endpoints and substitute the Fibonacci numbers for x: (x, x), $(-x, x)$, $(-x, -x)$, $(x, -x)$.